This & Suntouched written by Taffy (she is half welsh!), we were new girls together

PIPPA's ARK

NARRATED BY TRAYZER

THERESA NICHOLAS

Pen Press

© Theresa Nicholas 2012

All rights reserved

No part of this publication may be reproduced, stored in a retrieval system, or transmitted in any form or by any means, without the prior permission in writing of the publisher, nor be otherwise circulated in any form of binding or cover other than that in which it is published and without a similar condition including this condition being imposed on the subsequent purchaser.

First published in Great Britain

All paper used in the printing of this book has been made from wood grown in managed, sustainable forests.

ISBN13: 978-1-78003-314-3

Printed and bound in the UK
Pen Press is an imprint of
Indepenpress Publishing Limited
25 Eastern Place
Brighton
BN2 1GJ

A catalogue record of this book is available from the British Library

Cover design by Jacqueline Abromeit

Everything happens, but nothing ever stays. We live in a constant fluctuation of coming and going. What remains is only the eternal, that invisible trace that lovers, friends and children leave with you as a fragrance of their being.

Make your heart beat with the vanishing moments and everything will be transformed into poetry...your life will become a garland of many important and unique moments.

RUMI

In memory of
Pippa
and all the animals...

1.
Midsummer: St. John's Night

My neighbours' children have made three heaps of dried grass on the path. When it is dark they light them. You must jump the fires three times, they say, to leave your sins behind you, or for good luck, or something like that. The older women look on, but Maria, a sprightly young mother of two, joins in, saucily whisking her skirts aside from the flames with an adroit hand. There is plenty of gossip about her. She has a good husband who would rather turn a blind eye to her peccadilloes , than lose her. Not all Greek men are like that, mine certainly wasn't.

I jumped the fires for the first time tonight, then I leave them to it, climb the metal stair to my aerie to watch them from my balcony, their figures jumping through the smoke. The kids keep the fires going with dry grass, the orange flames quickly flare up and die down. As the night goes on the children get more and more daring. `I jumped it first when the fire was this high!' boasts little Phillipos.

They keep jumping to the screams of encouragement from other kids, and caution from the grandmothers, their ritual guardians. Two children collide and fall in the ashes, no real hurt. They chant something with a liturgical lilt to it, which seems as old as recorded time. How many centuries has this ceremony been enacted on this path? This is Greece not Surbiton. Below the surface lies the ancient town, 3.000 years of habitation, customs and rituals.

The children are still jumping the fires at 11 pm. Feeling rather alone, I turn my head and see Koko sitting in the open doorway, regarding me with pagan gold eyes. He knows he should not be up here...... My landlady, Rene, who lives below won't allow

1

me to have the dog upstairs, even though the approach to my separate flat is by an outside metal stairway.

'Why you want a dog! The hairs of the dog give you disease! In Greece, a dog is tied to a barrel to bark and keep foxes away from their chickens. They would never have a dog in the house. She likes cats – cats are clean, dogs are dirty. Even so, she doesn't let the cats into her house. They do not have the concept of animals as friends or pets.

While they are all busy with the fires, he has sneaked up the outside stair to my room. We regard each other in tacit collusion. When he understands I have courage tonight not to send him away, he lies down quietly and heaves a sigh of relief and sleeps.

Koko

Sometimes I wonder how I acquired this dog. It was not my intention. The only person who has dogs around here is Pippa, the English girl, who lives at the top of the Olive Grove. She collects dogs as a dog collects fleas. Only the English have animals as 'friends'. It was another English woman who turned up on my doorstep saying she was leaving the island and needed to find a home for a puppy she had been nurturing. 'He's four months old now…Pippa would have taken him, but she has gone back to England… as you know…'

I don't know Pippa personally, but I know her story, („no secrets on this island) – how she came on holiday, met and married her Greek, had a child and a lot of dogs, but had given up and returned to her country of origin.

'I'm sorry' I repeat, 'I don't want a dog.' I am not that sort of English woman – and being British resent having to 'be sorry' about it.

'But I thought it would be company for you now…' So she knows my story. No secrets on this island.

'I'm sorry,' (again, damn it!) 'I can't cope with anything except myself at present.'

Disappointed she went away. I thought that was the end of it, but a week later she was back on the doorstep again, this time the young dog was at her heels – black with a white shirt front and two white paws….a nice looking dog. 'But I do not want a dog,' I reiterate. Sadly she turned away and went to catch the bus to town from the road above the house. The dog went too. Two minutes later, the dog was back. Having seen his mistress onto the bus , like a gentleman (no possibility of taking a dog on a Greek bus) he dashed back down the path and up the metal stair into my kitchen and into my life.

We looked at each other. He smiled. I accepted defeat.

Koko smiling

I did not really know what to do with this new companion. I did not know how to talk to him. We went for silent walks – that was good. I had more confidence with a dog to wander about the olive groves alone. A woman on her own, especially a foreign one, is an object of conjecture. `Ti theli afti ?' *(What is she looking for...?)* A woman is supposed to belong to a man, just as the dog now belongs to me. Even the men are afraid of dogs......
I wasn't sure that the whole thing hadn't been arranged by *him* from beyond the grave. It is so characteristic....

There were moments last summer when I lost his image, and even wondered if he had existed. But he would assert himself in some brilliant image in a dream, just a flash, but something so positive as to leave no doubt of his existence. The gap between the grave and his personality gets wider all the time.

When I look back on the months I've been living alone, it seems a long time, a long distance rather I have travelled in that time, longer than last Summer. I seem like a curled leaf lying on a slow moving stream turning gently this way and that with no destination except its own disappearance. But apart from drifting on the slow moving stream, the other part of me travels widely in depth and space, freer than ever before to move where I choose in the past and the present.

I had to go to England that Christmas. Poor Koko – there was nobody to look after him. I had to leave him to his own devices. After all, he had been foisted on me as the only option. I chucked him a bone, and said, "Sorry, Pal! " and went off to England, never expecting to see him again.

On my return, I walked with apprehension up the path `He won't be there... and what will I do without him now...' Suddenly I saw the black shape sliding up the path ahead of me. `Koko!' He turned, realising who it was, threw himself at me, grabbing my wrist in his mouth, weeping and sobbing for joy. We sat on the doorstep, cuddling each other. After our emotional reunion, he detached himself saying `Well, I'm off to get my breakfast now....' and beetles up to the taverna at the top of the path. I soon found that they dote on him, chucking him chunks of prime steak as they trim the meat for cooking. I was surprised, too, by my 'anti-dog' neighbours , each claiming to have fed him the most. Even Rene said `I gave him more bones than `she' did..' indicating with a nod, her sister-in-law, Effie, in the house next door. He is now a full member of our small neighbourhood, comprising half a dozen houses. No other dog has achieved that status. It is due to his personality alone.

As for our relationship, I do not have him as a pet. Rather, I am his person; all he needs from me is love and fellowship.

When Rene would not let me have the dog in the flat upstairs, I went to Eftihea, Rene's sister-in-law. She was our landlady when *he* and I lived next door to where I am now. The two do not get on. When she understood that Rene would not let me have the dog, she said, "Of course, you must have the dog if you want it. We will find a big box for him to sleep in. I will ask Anna " (another neighbour) " if you can put it at the back of her house. " A bit of land behind the house which contains an apricot tree and nothing else. " It is used for nothing. He can sleep there, and he will be near you. " Anna was willing and now Koko waits like Romeo under my balcony for me to appear.

2.

LAZARUS

Queer days these, filled with the lassitude of grief. In the evenings I go up to the taverna at the top of the path for an ouzo or a beer, and to be with Koko, as I must not have him up in my place.

The taverna is run by a Greek with an Italian wife who does all the cooking. They both love Koko. I have seen Spiro chuck him a whole steak when he's preparing the meat for the evening. Koko does very well at the tavern – and spends the evening begging around the tables, and gets all the left-overs at the end. I don't have to feed him at all. Now I am on my own I don't eat much, so there's not much left over for him and there is no such thing as 'dog food' in the shops. He doesn't do very well out off me. but he knows how to survive and doesn't look to me to feed him.

It was pleasant sitting outside in the early evening with Koko stretched out asleep at my feet, and chatting with Gabriella when she emerges from the kitchen for a breather from the cooking.

It was on just such an evening, that Lazarus appeared. A long legged boney bodied dog the colour of liver stopped by the gate and looked in sadly – not daring to enter. He was about to pass on when his amber eyes fixed on the form of Koko, sound asleep at my feet. Looking nervously to left and right, expecting at any moment to be threatened, he tiptoed cautiously down the steps from the road, until he stood over Koko. Koko feeling a presence, woke up – recognised this strange dog, and sprang up to greet him with a whoop of joy! They began to play like a couple of pups, tumbling about, mock fighting and clowning, until Spiros came out to see what the noise was, and drove the other dog away. I was surprised, as he is so kind to Koko.

"Him *Adespoti.* " meaning a stray dog – a dog without a master. Customers would be put off at the sight of two dogs mock fighting in the forecourt; particularly such a baleful looking dog as Lazarus.

When the customers begin to arrive, I go home. Koko, like a gentleman, sees me to the bottom of my stairs, and then goes back to the taverna on his own.

A couple of nights after the meeting between Lazarus and Koko, I was lying awake when I heard a dog cough. I went to look over the balcony and saw the strange dog whom I had instantly named Lazarus. He coughed again – quite discreetly. To my surprise, Koko came out to greet him and off they went together.

Lazarus comes most nights now – I hear him cough – and off they go. But Koko is always there in the morning waiting for me under the balcony. Koko is learning many things from Lazarus....

Lazarus

One day, when Koko for some reason was not with me, I walked up the olive grove alone, looking for him and feeling rather lonely, sat down under an olive tree to do some sketching. Suddenly Lazarus appeared and straightaway curled himself up against me and went to sleep, as if he knew I needed company.

There were moments last summer when I lost *his* image, and even wondered if he had existed. But he would assert himself in some brilliant image in a dream, just a flash, but something so positive as to leave no doubt of his existence. The gap between the grave and the recreated personality gets wider all the time.

Last week I bought a bicycle, a bright orange bicycle, but I have to have a license to ride it. The old man who has the shop came with me to the Town Hall, took me to the right office – I would never have found it for myself. Forms were made out with Father's name, Mothers' name and I had to supply two photographs, just like a passport. I was told to come back in 4-5 days. Until I have the license I must not ride the bike, so I had to leave it at the shop. After three abortive trips to the Town Hall, I got my license, a small white booklet with Father's name, Mother's name and my name all written in the English alphabet so no Greek Policeman could read it, and with my photo affixed to it. With this in my hand, I went back to the shop to claim my new bicycle. 'Ah,' said the old man ,' you must to have a number plate.' A number plate for a bicycle? He was stumped how to explain to me where I must go to get the number plate made up. It was somewhere deep in the centre of the old town. How was I to find it? Another man in the shop obligingly consented to show me. It was deep in the rabbit warren of the old town. He took me into a very small print shop where they think it is a Driving License book I need. No, we need a number plate for a bicycle. Oh, -that's another shop, along there, down there, and up this little alley. Finally we enter a Typographer's shop. 'You want a bicycle plate? No problem. The man, was in process of binding a little book, but he took some blue self-adhesive paper, and with a pair of scissors skillfully cut out the three numbers: 9 5 4. From under a pile of papers, he took a tin plate with **KEPKYPA 75** on it and stuck the numbers onto the space below. Won't they come off in the rain, I wondered. Probably.

But , finally, I have a number plate for which I have to pay 50 drs. Quite a lot, but at last, I can take possession of my bicycle and ride it home.

Koko trots by my bike now when I go to the cemetery. Sometimes I have to put him on the lead. At first his nervous jolts pulled me off the bike but he makes sudden advances in techniques. Once he understands what I want him to do, he does it. I can't say I train him. Suddenly he begins to behave the way I want him to behave which shows how intelligent he is. We go for a walk in the afternoon. He is always waiting below my window, I can't let him down. This afternoon an hilarious courtship scene between Koko and a young bitch who looks exactly like him, black mongrel with white paws. She is tied to a tree on the hill . Her mother, an old fat dog, sits by her. I don't know why they are there, or who they belong to. Koko has been interested in her for days. This is the first time he has found her alone except for her mother. Usually `Old Bollocks' a big stray dog, is guarding her too, waiting for the moment. Today no sign of Bollocks.

Koko approached with caution, expecting Bollocks to appear. The young bitch acts coy and welcoming, but when he gets too close, the old mother dog barks at him. The two lovers managed a couple of kisses, before Koko, backing off, gives a manly performance of barking and scuffing up the earth in clods from his back legs. His barks ricocheted off the walls of the block of flats below. He thought it was another dog and decided not to try things further.

This morning I was sitting with Mrs. Toms. having an ouzo on the Esplanade. Koko was with me. Suddenly Lazarus, that strange mongrel, appeared. So he comes into town, does he? He saw Koko first, then me and flung his forefeet into my lap. Koko, though Lazarus is his friend, jumped up barking and snarling with jealousy. They were ready to fight over possession of me. 'Quite like old times!' I exclaim, ' Is this my destiny? Even Greek dogs are jealous?' Mrs. Toms laughed.

There are the 'Alice in Wonderland' encounters with people who know me but have never spoken to me before. Nitza , a portly ugly little woman, middle-aged, talks to me about life, love death, man and woman etc. 'Don't you want to marry now?' 'What for?' I say. In England this would be very embarrassing but here they are far more realistic about life. It is a question of attitudes. She tells me she is divorced and has another man. A little embarrassed she says, 'But we live like brother and sister...' with a little gesture picking up her skirt with her finger and letting it drop to denote nothing passes that way. She takes me to light candles at the little chapel of St. Paraskevi, along the road. A little whitewashed chapel deep in buttercups and green green grass with a sentinel cypress beside it.

An old woman lives beside in a shack with some chickens, a sheep and a goat. She looks after the chapel as a grace and favour occupation. She recognised Nitza and made coffee for us. We went into the chapel to light candles. Nitza prevented me putting the money in the offertory box, indicating to leave it on the shelf so the old woman can have it, not the Pappas. I love details like this. ~

Felicity is here.. In her seventies now, a Botanical artist, who wins medals for her flower paintings, she describes herself as ` a fairly ordinary Middle-class Englishwoman'. She has been on the mainland digging up Colchicums and Liliums which she takes back to England to exhibit these rare species at the Horticultural Society This time she has a bad back and is confined to bed in a hotel in town. `I broke my back years ago when my horse threw me. It plays up from time to time. Jolly annoying.'

I cycle to town to keep her company in the evening. Koko and Lazarus chaperone me, bounding along on either side of the bike. I stay with her till about 10 o'clock, yet when I come back to the bike in the alleyway, one of the dogs has stayed to guard it, while the other has gone off to cadge some supper from one of the restaurants. One night Koko is on duty, another night it will be Lazarus.

From Felicity I learn more about the English girl, Pippa. She knows Pippa's mother.

`She went to England thinking to take a Teacher training course. Her father was prepared to buy her a house in Norwich, so she could rent rooms to University students, but her mother says, she pined so much for the island, she is coming back. Should be here any time now. At least, she still has the house . It was up for sale, but nobody wanted it. '

When I was in town this morning shopping, I popped up to see her for half an hour. Looking over the balcony of her room, I saw the girl, Pippa, walking toward the hotel, holding her small boy by the hand – obviously coming up to see Felicity. Sure enough, they walked into the room. She looked radiant and confident. "You can tell Mother I haven't been so happy for a long time. It's going to be all right, I've been offered a job in a tourist agency during the summer."

Pippa and Lol

Apart from a brief nod in my direction she took no notice of me. After all, we don't know each other, though we share the experience of this island. The blonde kid grizzled a bit, bored by it all. I'm not interested in children. Never wanted any.

"And you can tell her, Ben is alright." she went on, "Athéna fed him."

I guessed Ben is one of her dogs. It explained an encounter in the olive grove, with a pug-nosed black and white dog whom Koko recognised and immediately kowtowed to by rolling on his back and putting his paws in the air. He seemed thrilled to see him, but the older dog refused to acknowledge the young dog and passed on with pompous dignity.

"Oh, you mean `Chairman Mao' as I used to call him." Felicity said. It described the dog perfectly.

Ben "Chairman Man"

Felicity is leaving tomorrow; I went to see her this evening and stayed till eleven o'clock. When I came back to the bike it had been raining heavily, but there was Lazurus, sopping wet, curled up tight guarding it. No sign of Koko – he must have gone back to Spiros and Gaby for supper.
I rode home through thunder and lightning with my strange companion bounding along beside me. I was glad of his company and he seemed thrilled to be doing me this service. He saw me right to my staircase before he would leave.
"Thank you, Lazarus, you are a real Gentleman.
I cant help feeling there is something occult going on here. *He* never let me go anywhere alone.... especially at night.

Saw Felicity off at the airport. Pippa came too, with the child. We went up to the new balcony lounge because the kid wanted to see what he called the `H'airyplanes'. We waved to Felicity as she walked painfully across the Tarmac to board the plane. As we parted, Pippa said, `Come up and see us...... .'
`Yes – I'd like to....'' and heard myself saying, `and ... if you need some help with him, you can always dump on me for an hour or two.' *What did I mean by that?* The next day she did.
I heard their footsteps on the path, and looking over my balcony saw the young woman with the long brown hair and the blond headed child. She looked up, `Do you think you could take him for a couple of hours? I've got to go to town......'
` Okay....' I've never done this before.
`You'll be alright, won't you, Lol?' consulting the child, who nodded, climbing the metal stair, more interested in the stairway than where it would take him. As he arrives in the kitchen I ask, `What's your name?' We have not been introduced.
`My name is Lawrence – but I'm called Lollipop, ' he says seriously. So that's why she called him `Lol'
I had no experience of children. I didn't know what to do with him, but I didn't have to do anything. He set about examining everything in my small Pad, handling everything with care, his scrutiny intense. He was particularly interested in my foldable artist's easel, wanted to know what it was for, exactly how it worked, and very soon had adapted it into a `pretend' telescope pointing it out of the window, and then turning it into

a `pretend' machine gun. When he had had enough of that, he suddenly said,

"Don't you want to come up to my house? I could *Show you Things...*"

The invitation was irresistible. Followed by Koko, we took the path up through the olive grove, to where Pippa's garden appeared on a high bank; the path led right into it, no fence or gate. At the garden's edge under the big Nettle tree, `Chairman Mao', watched our invasion disapprovingly, but because we as we were with Lawrence – he didn't protest, simply turning away in disgust.

Soon I was sitting the floor in Lawrence's bedroom being shown his collection of cars, while he made brummm...brummm....noises.That is how it all began.

3.

PADDINGTON

It has become natural to wander up to Pippa's in the afternoons, climbing the steep grove of gesticulating olive trees. A block of new flats is being built at the bottom on the road, but I can find my way through the building site to get into the olive grove, and enter Pippa's garden by the Nettle tree. Whatever I find them doing, I join in – listening to a story, playing trains or stay with him while she goes off to town to meet her friends, or do some shopping.

As I walked in one afternoon, Pippa said,' Look what we've got.'

Sitting on the sofa wrapped in a crocheted blanket was a small shaggy brown puppy. 'Jan has just brought him. She saw a man stuffing him into a plastic bag to throw him into the sea. That's how they dispose of pups. So she took him.'

'Why doesn't she keep him?'

'She's got too many already, that's why she brought him to us. I acquire all my animals this way. Whenever somebody saves a puppy or a kitten they bring them to me. They know English people like animals better than people.'

We stood around looking at the puppy. The puppy looked forlornly back at us, wondering what this translation in his circumstances might mean.

'He looks just like Paddington Bear.' said Lol. 'We are going to keep him, aren't we, mummy?' There was no doubt about it.

In 24 hours all trace of forlorness had disappeared from Paddington. He was bouncing up and down, wanting the other dogs to play with him, but it was beneath their dignity to do so. Chairman Mao distained to notice the intruder. Koko, too, refused to play with him...

Koko refusing to play with puppy

...until, one afternoon, I saw Koko in the garden with Paddy bouncing around him barking 'Come on!! Play with me!! I want to play!!' Koko glanced furtively toward the house, seeing no-one, threw his dignity to the winds to appease the little brat.

Koko playing with puppy

Pippa and Lawrence went back to England for Christmas, leaving me in charge of the animals. The dogs, the cat, the budgerigars, the Love Bird and the Hamsters. I went up to the house every morning to let the dogs out and, in the evening, to feed them and shut them up again.

One night, having let Paddy out into the garden to do his nightly pee – I lost him! I called and called – no response. I grabbed up the torch, flashing around wildly and caught him in its beam doing a splendid pee, holding his leg up as high as it would go, and there between his legs sat an enormous toad lugubriously regarding the stream that just missed his nose. It was one of the biggest toads I have ever seen.

I laughed over the image for days.

Paddy peeing on a toad

4.

THE LOVE BIRD

The love bird

I have never felt easy with caged birds, and never understood how human beings , appreciating that birds fly in the air, want to capture them and put them in cages and I hate to see the cage traps set to catch Robins and Finches.. I find the song of canaries witless. Pippa did not keep her birds in this way. The Budgies were dumped on her, by someone is leaving the island promising it will only be for a short time – which means `forever'.

In the same way, she acquired a pair of Love birds, with beady knowing eyes, green plumage and bright red breasts. It was obvious from the first that they were in a very different category of intelligence from canaries and budgerigars. She started off with two – I cannot remember what happened to one of them – it must have died of natural causes, so we had one left, called "Visigoth" by Lawrence who must have been reading Asterix.

One does not expect to be psychologically challenged by a Love Bird, but I came up to the house one morning to find the Budgies cage empty, and Visigoth sitting in his cage waiting for breakfast with the door of his cage open. This was mystifying. When I challenged him, he eyed me with a boot button eye. For a moment I wondered if the Budgies cage had been empty when I brought it in the night before. Was I going potty? No, I remember I had fed them. So where were they now? Pippa often lets them fly around the room, but there was no sign of them. Then I saw I had left a window open. and remember Pippa saying that on one occasion, the Love bird had managed to undo the door of his cage and get out, but not only that, he had gone to the Budgies cage and opened the door for them.

"You little Devil! You've done it again. And where are they now? The stupid things are done for."

He didn't give a damn. He had the sense to get his freedom, use it, and come back to his cage for breakfast. The poor stupid Budgies were not in the same league, they could never find their way home.

"Okay! I am going to *screw you up tight.*"

I found a piece of wire and wired up the door to his cage. Sitting calmly on his perch, he watched what I was doing with his beady eye. Having done it, I went into the kitchen. Two minutes later, I surprised him at the cage door trying to untwist the wire with his strong parrot like beak. "You devil!" overawed by his intelligence.

Every time I opened the cage to feed him, he watched me untwist the wire, and watched every move of my fingers as I twisted it up tight again. The moment my back was turned, he was at it, trying to undo it. You have to respect intelligence like that. I had to use my intelligence to defeat his. If he had been my bird, loving freedom for myself, I would have had to let him go to his own perdition.

One day he wasn't there any more. He had managed it, and this time he didn't come home for breakfast.

5.

'PIPPA'S ARK'

I have labeled Pippa's place "Pippa's Ark". Pippa was a practical person to whom other people came looking for solutions, and she was very good at solving other people's problems, but it was not her way to take practical action against any form of animal life. Pippa never saw anything relating to animal life a being a problem. Apart from dogs, cats, Budgies, Love Birds and a rabbit, there were the uninvited intrusive guests – i.e. rats and mice

The mice made their nests in her drawers and cupboards. and took over the larder. Of course they were not ordinary mice either –

`They're only field mice…' said Pippa.

It was a small larder with steep narrow shelves and a sliding door. They came in through a small window from the overgrown hedge outside. But they quickly learned the benefits of the well stocked vegetarian larder and bit their way into everything, puncturing the plastic milk cartons, like vampires, to drink from the fountain of Long Life Milk.

Finding myself in the larder eyeball to eyeball with a tiny creature who scuttled behind the packets of lentils, I would thrash about shouting `You wretched little devils! Get out of here!'.

I began to fantasize about them, making up a story to amuse Lawrence, about the Mice who ate the beans, and with the resulting blast off, discover themselves levitating around the kitchen. He was delighted with this story and called it `The Farting Mice' and carried it a stage further. `They could make a capsule out of the empty plastic milk bottles, and fart their way to the Moon, Trayzer!' So we invented the story of `The Farting Mice' who ate the beans and with the results, realized they could do what MAN HAD DONE – fart their way to the Moon. ANYTHING MAN DO – MOUSE CAN DO! This story kept us busy for a whole winter.

The more I studied the mice in the larder, the more respect I had for them. It changed my attitude entirely. One morning – sliding open the larder door, knowing there would be a scuttle of tiny feet. Sure enough, there was a mouse on the shelf right in front of me, so I said, ` Good morning, Mouse!' in a benign voice. The reaction was extraordinary. Instead of scuttling for cover – anticipating my customary greeting of `Drat you Mice – Get Out of Here Quick!' and banging about, he was transfixed by this new mode of greeting. For a long moment we looked at each other. `*What's come over her....?'* I could see him thinking, before he panicked and dove for cover. ~~

I must say the cat did his best. He spent hours in that larder gazing up at the steep narrow shelves, lashing his tail from side to side in frustration – in making a leap upwards would find himself hanging by his fingernails in impotent rage as the saucy mice flicked out of sight behind the packets and plastic cartons. Poor cat! The terrain was difficult.

Then there were the rats. . The rats walk the tightrope of the electric cable from the gate to the corner of the roof punctually at sundown, summer and winter. Pippa always maintains that they are harmless `fruit rats'. Certainly they gorge on the oranges in the tree in front of the house, knowing where to go for their Vitamin C.

I observed a rat closely one afternoon through the kitchen window. The dogs' bowl had some food in it. The rat reached into the deep dish with a sensitive hand to scoop out whatever was left, and raised it to his mouth. It was such a human action, it made me wonder. Hadn't I read somewhere that the human species evolved from tree rats, after the fall of the dinosaurs....?

When Pippa could afford it, a wood burning stove was installed in the kitchen, with its pipe going through the wooden ceiling into the roof. When it was alight, we could hear the rats above our heads squeaking and fighting for the best places around the warm pipe.

A rat moved into my roof one summer. I had moved from Rene's to the penthouse on top of Effie's place next door. The corrugated roof being not far above my head, it sounded as if the rat had taken up its lodging in my brain. Every night at 9 pm precisely it whipped over the balcony coping and disappeared. Returning in the early hours of morning scrabbling in the corrugated roof above my head. It had its baby in the roof.

One day when Lawrence was with me, I was telling him about my rats, the mother and child. To my surprise he said, `I can see it.' He was just outside on the terrace looking up at the low rain gutter. Sure enough a ratty little face was peering over the edge. `Quick – Trayzer! we can get it!' It was the baby rat. I got a big tin, held it in the gutter while he herded the creature into it. Having caught it we were both perplexed. `What are we going to do with it, Trayzer?' I had a big glass honey jar, we got it into that. I perforated the lid so it could breathe. Lawrence sat for a long time watching the young rat-ling sliding around in the glass jar – it was *so beautiful*. One never thinks a rat can be beautiful. It was.

`What shall we do with it, Trayzer?'
Again the question: *To let Be, or not to Let Be....*
In the end we took it down the path and released it into the undergrowth. `Perhaps his mum will find him...'
She must have gone looking for him. I never saw or heard her again.

6.

THE GRYPHON

Paddington has grown from the tiny ragged-haired pup, saved from drowning, into a strong ragged-haired dog. One day he was waiting for Pippa outside a shop, a tourist lady was looking at him with great attention. When Pippa appeared , the lady asked, "Is that your dog ?" "Yes..... why?" "But he's a Gryphon!" "A what?" `A Gryphon." "What's that?" thinking of some sort of effigy. "It's a rare breed of French hunting dog. " Pippa laughed, "But he's only a local mongrel."

Challenged in her knowledge of dog species, the lady insisted on taking Pippa's name and address, and sent her a photograph of a pure bred Gryphon. It was the spitting image of our Paddy.

"Look, Paddy – its you. You're a Gryphon." He was not impressed. He was himself with occasional impersonations of Stalin. (Chairman Mao had disappeared by now).

Paddington as "Stalin"

The breed must have been brought to this island during the French occupation in the last century and fed their genes into the local population. But it is true Paddy was unlike any other mongrel type. That is what makes our mongrel dogs so special and of such fine intelligence – worth all the stupid pedigree dogs in the world.

Pippa leaves the house early to drop Lawrence off at the School on her way to work. At the same time the dogs, Paddy, Snoopy, Nellie, joined sometimes by Koko and Lazarus, set out on their morning round of the garbage bags. There are no rubbish bins yet, everybody throws their plastic bags of rubbish by the road, a lorry comes round to pick them up. So the stray dogs and cats can find a varied menu: macaroni in tomato sauce, chicken bones, beef bones, Moussaka, and pastitzatha, bits of fish..... a restaurant could not serve a more varied menu. Corfiote dogs laugh at the notion that chicken bones are bad for them – their survivor genes can cope with anything – except rat poison. Every morning Pippa's dogs would set off on the breakfast rubbish round.

Bicycling into town, I dread meeting them . "Oh, look there's Trayzer! Trayzer! Wait for us...Trayzer " they shout, galloping boisterously after me as I peddle as fast as I can to get away from them. "We're coming with you...." enjoying the extra exercise of keeping up with me. What fun!

It ruins my shopping morning. I must go to the Bank. Paddy follows me in. No longer a puppy, he is a man of world and appoints himself my chaperone. `I must look after you, Trayzer.'

The reaction in the Bank is immediate. Everybody in the queue starts flinging their arms about like windmills, shouting "Oxó! Oxó!" then turning on me, "Is it yours?" "No.... he's not with me. He's an Adespoti (a stray, or more literally `without a despot) and whispering furiously at Paddy. "Get out Paddy..... Oxó! Oxó!" Their absurd word for getting rid of dogs, which sounds so much like our Oxo cubes. He sits down on his bottom.

"Trayzer, why are you saying that? That's what They say..."
"Because I'm a coward. I'm not Pippa ,who isn't!"

"But it is my duty to protect you..."

"Go A-Way, Paddy. Pleeeeze... SHOO!"

He goes with dignity, but sits vigilantly outside gazing in through the glass doors, making his eyes all slitty in his imitation of Stalin, refusing to get out of way of people trying to leave or enter the bank who all consider him to be the most dangerous of monsters.

When I emerge my canine friends greet me again with joy, as if I have been released from some terrible ordeal. They know about living on a crust. Don't they do it every morning ? They don't want to rely on Pippa for everything. They know the strain on her purse, she has Lawrence to support. All they really want from us is LOVE, and are prepared to draw a blind over my betrayal just now in the Bank.

My shopping expedition progresses with me betraying them all the time, as they try follow me into shops , determined not to lose sight of me. Though driven out by the eternal "Oxó! Oxó!" they see me safely home to their world, our world, Pippa and Lawrence's world. A job well done!~~

7.

LADY NELLIE BELLINGTON

Nobody could say Nellie was of superior intelligence. All she was interested in was sleep and food. Maybe that was because she was the first to have the benefit of being spayed. But she went with the boys on the breakfast round , she could fight alongside them, and lifted her leg the boy's way. The rest of the day she slept until supper time. She had been found a plastic bag on the path near my place. It was the Summer we had Pippa's sister, Penny and her baby son Gwillie with us. They had been down to see my place, and we were on our way back to their place, just like Pooh and Piglet. I walked past the bag without noticing what it contained, but Penny and Lawrence did not. " Trayzer... " I looked back to see them standing beside the plastic bag, which I had presumed to contain rubbish. "There's a puppy in the bag. " A liver and white smooth haired pup was looking out of the blue plastic bag. " What shall we do with it, Trayzer?" There was only one thing to do with it – take it up to Pippa's place.

"I wonder what Mummy will say, " said Lawrence already playing with the puppy in his bedroom.
 "It's a girl," said Penny.

When Pippa came home after dark, Lawrence hurled himself on her in his usual way to give her a hug and a kiss. "Mummee...." he says in that way that instantly alerts her. "What is it, Lol?" He thinks how to put it and comes up with "We've got a "visitor".."
 Her instant response: "How many legs has it got?"
 "Four...." he cautiously replies.

"Oh, that's all right – lets have a look at it..."
He pulls the puppy out from under the bed in his room. "Oh, what a poppet!" she says, immediately taking it up to cuddle it.

Nellie as a puppy

"It's a girl...." we offer the information dubiously.

"Oh, that doesn't matter. We can have her spayed later on, now we have an English Vet on the island."

Greek Vets dealt with cows, pigs, goats, sheep, and donkeys, not pets. But recently an Englishwoman had come to live on the island, who was a practicing Veterinary surgeon and Nellie was "done" on the kitchen table with Pippa acting as assistant. "At one time I wanted to be a vet," she says.

Perhaps it was her operation that made Nellie such a silly lovable animal, who never grew up. She got fatter that's all, and acquired the name, "Jelly Belly" and later " Nellie Jellie Belly" and finally `Lady Jellybellington.' as she spent hours reclining on the sofa...

Addicted to sleep, she contrived so many different postures during the course of a whole day, (after the breakfast run). To fill the time till supper, she would sleep, and sleep and sleep. She did not even dream – she never twitched or whimpered as the others did. Her dreams, if she had any were of perfect relaxation, but at the first hint of supper, she was awake and into the kitchen like a flash.

Nellie full grown

She had a funny way of putting her paw in her dish to keep it from sliding around while she scoffed the contents in three seconds flat. ~~

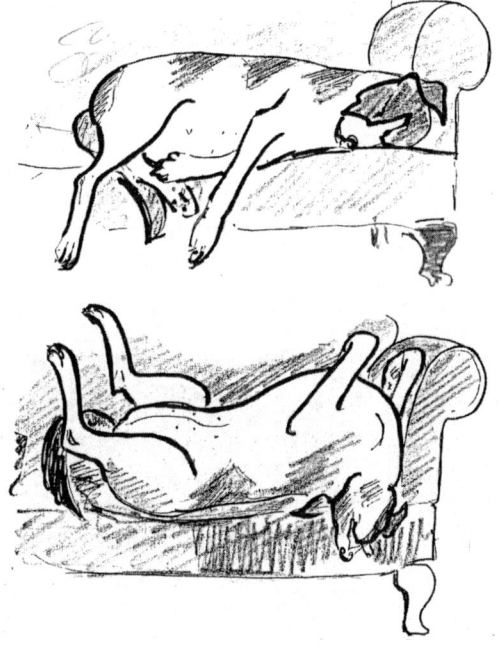

Nellie sleeping on sofa

8.

GANGA

That first summer when Lawrence was small and still called Lollipop, I wondered how Pippa would cope. "What will you do with him while you're working during the summer season?" It was not a 9-5 job. She had to take tourists on Taverna Nights in Summer.

"Oh, it won't be a problem," she said blithely, " Mother will come out for three months. She'll stay until it gets too hot – then we'll find something ...." She was flying by the seat of her pants, but was happy and confident that it would all work out. And it did ... (and when it didn't – there was always Me.)

We go to the Airport to meet Joan, known as "Ganga" instead of Granny. Lol jumped up and down with excitement "There she IS!" he shouted, as a small slight woman with a large bag on one shoulder came nimbly down the aircraft steps and across the Tarmac. As we rushed round to wait outside the Arrivals watching the people within through the glass doors.

"Lol, don't call out when she comes, right? We mustn't wave," cautioned Pippa. "Why?" "She's bringing something, and the Customs men mustn't suspect or they'll stop her. If they see us waving, they'll know she isn't an ordinary tourist."

It was agonizing for Lol – until she emerged pushing a trolley with an enormous Teddy Bear sitting on it. Lol sprang at her, "Ganga!" and nearly had her over.

"Have you got it?" Pippa asked. "Yes – Feel the weight of it –" indicating the bag she had been carrying nonchalantly on one shoulder. It weighed a ton.

"What is it?" I ask.

"An electric sewing machine."

"Well done, Mother," said Pippa. "but what's that?" indicating the large Teddy Bear – like an obese 5 year old.

"His father rang me late last night, asking could I bring out something for Lol. I had no idea what it was until he came to the airport with it. It needed seat to itself. It was most embarrassing."

Pippa and her Greek husband had virtually swopped countries. He preferred the opportunities Britain offered; she preferred the simple life Greece offered "An excellent arrangement," she says. ~~

9.

EASTER

It was Easter when Ganga came. We watched the Good Friday procession set out from the little church that overlooks Pippa's garden. ["Nobody wanted to buy the two old peasant cottages, because they are overlooked by the graveyard. We got them cheap and renovated them ourselves."]

The funeral procession for Christ in the Greek Orthodox mode has a picturesque melancholy all its own. The black wooden cross, the simple catafalque like a tea trolley decorated with wisteria, is carried on the shoulders of the boys. The procession sets off down the hill led by the Band in their blue and red uniforms, brass helmets and gleaming instruments playing mournful music, followed by four to six male singers, and the parishioners carrying lighted candles and the Pappás carrying the Bible.

At certain intervals, comes the *caesura* – the pause – the instruments silent, the men's voices cleave the silence with the Virgin's lament for her son. It haunts the whole evening, as each church makes its own funeral procession for Christ. It fills the air like a gas permeating everything, as well as oozing out of the stonework.

The next morning ,Saturday, we go down to the town for the "Pot Throwing".

"What does it mean?" Lol asks. "Nobody really knows. Some say its stoning Judas.' "Who's Judas?" Oh, here we go – explain Judas. "The bloke who's supposed to have betrayed Jesus." Lol frowns trying to take this in. "Why did he...?" "You'll get to know about when you go to School – anyway that may not be the reason at all. Some say if you break a pot on this day at 11 o'clock when they take the Saint back into the Church, it gets rid of your sins and brings good luck."

Lol frowns again, brewing up another unanswerable question. "But is he real.... that Saint?"

"Well he was real, now he's been dead for over 1,000 years. They did special things to his body and he's still working miracles, they say.... "

"What's a mirrakul?"

"Oh, Lor, – Ganga – how do you cope with this sort of thing."

"You just have to try. It goes on and on until they start telling you where you got it all wrong, and were talking nonsense."

We got to the main square just as the bells rang out at 11 o'clock. "Watch that one, Lol," pointing up to a balcony where a couple of young men had a huge pot poised on the balcony. Down it came making an most satisfying explosion. Lol jumped up and down with glee as pots of all sizes and shapes were flung with abandon into the street covering it with broken shards.

"There's a story that before the War a cruise ship with German tourists came into the port on this particular morning. They walked up to see the town but hearing the explosions and seeing all the broken pottery and the butchers were running around slaughtering the sheep for the next days feast – with blood all over them and knives in scabbards. They fled back to the ship, thinking it was a revolution.. you can imagine it, can't you."

Going up the narrow alleys after it is over, Lawrence stamps on the broken shards with the satisfaction of a child stamping in puddles. This way he doesn't notice the bodies of three sheep with their throats cut, blood seeping into the gutter, watched by a group of small children. Lol busily stamping, suddenly stops, seeing at his feet a tiny porcelain tea cup, still intact except for the handle. Bystanders watching him urge him to stamp on it. He doesn't. "Oh, No!" he says, "Its TOO Luvely isn't it, Ganga? Isn't it, Trayzer..?." picking it up. "I want to take it home....can't I?" Now he is sorry for all the `poor pots' that have been broken. "They are poor , aren't they.... to get all broken like that. I'm going to keep this one for ever and ever... aren't we?"

Making me wonder why we have to grow up. ~~

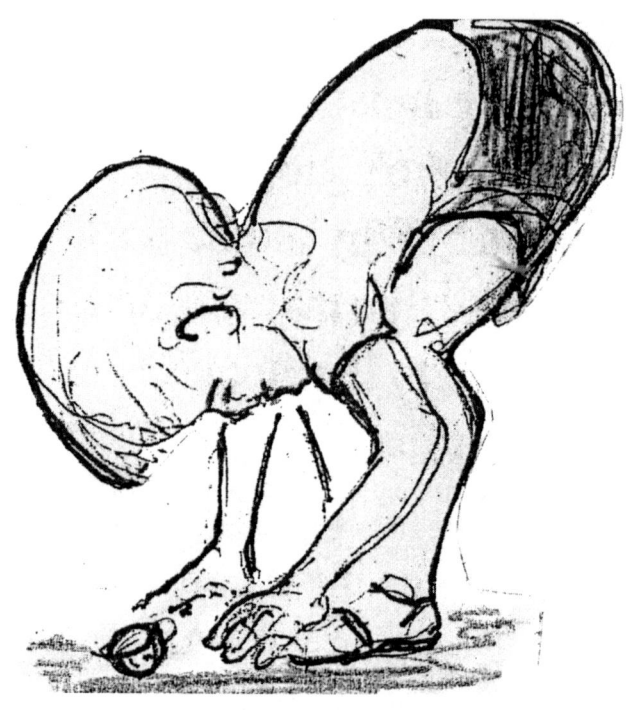

16: Lol picking up the cup

Easter Sunday – Pippa being a vegetarian, we escape the ritual guzzling of roasted sheep by driving up the mountain, with a vegetarian picnic, to be alone among the Hermes oaks, and ilex nipped and topiaried by herds of goats. Rocks litter the landscape like monstrous teeth – it is another world from the gesticulating Olive groves and the villages and the town where the sheep are turning on the spits. Up here the sheep are still on their feet. There are goat paths leading in among the rocks to small pastures like rooms walled in by wind sculpted ilex. On the highest peak, standing up like a nipple, is the monastery, out of which ,in this modern age, grows the giant radio mast soaring into the sky. It wasn't there when I came to the island in 1961. Out of this grows another story – like the mice in the larder. SNAPDRAGON'S WAR – *the war of the ninety – hundred- thousand – million Bees, Bugs, Bats, rats, fleas, ticks, Mice, lice, wasps, hornets who rise up against mankind's desecration of the natural world with its infernal devices and abominable litter.* War always appeals to children.

We picnic at a stone table with stone stools outside an old sheepcote from which come an incessant bleating. Peering in we see a pen full of kids with their delicate slit nostrils and amber pagan eyes staring back at us. "You're the lucky ones!" we tell them.

Buzzards cruise high overhead as we search for wild orchids among the rocks and find them. Wheatears, and Red Back Shrikes flash briefly on our retinas. The mountains of the mainland present themselves like the backs of dinosaurs across a brilliant blue sea. It is hard to leave this so different world, to descend to where the fires have burned out and the sheep have been consumed. Easter has come and gone.....

10.

RUPERT RABBIT

A few days later, Ganga told me, "Pippa has had a rabbit dumped on her. Supposed to be temporary – but you know what she's like. Lawrence has called it `Rupert-rabbit', after the story, you know. He always takes it out of its cage when he comes home, carrying it about, stroking its long ears before letting it loose in the sitting room.

The telephone rang. Pippa answered it. "Yes – by all means come up." she said to somebody. Turning to Lol, she said, "Better put the rabbit back in its cage, Lol – Melanie's coming up, ..so we don't want anything unusual happening .She's bringing a friend....to tea."

"What sort of a friend?" he asks suspiciously.

"A Boy Friend."

"Will there be chocolate cake?" Pippa had just made a chocolate cake. She hadn't made one like that for ages.

"Yes." So he put the rabbit back in his box.

Melanie arrived just he was coming back into the kitchen. He heard her say, "And here's Rupert..."

"Where?" exclaimed Lol , as he had just put Rupert back in his box.

"Melanie's friend is called Rupert," said Pippa.

"A Person can't be called Rupert!" says Lol. "It's a rabbit's name!"

We all started talking mostly at cross purposes to fill the vacuum. Lawrence got bored – wondering why didn't they get down the serious business of the Chocolate cake. Given his slice, he was eating slowly the way he does anything really scrumptiousness. He always likes to take his pleasure slowly, totally impervious to what is going on around him. Suddenly he said, "Rupert's got lovely long ears....." thinking of his rabbit. The young man's hand went straight to his rather large red ear.

"He smells nice too...." went on Lol following his own line of thought.

The young man blushing said, "It's After-shave – a birthday present."

I was having real difficulty keeping a straight face, when Lawrence said, "I don't like After-`save'...When I grow up I shall NEVER wear After `save'. Its not nearly so nice as rabbit."

Pippa managed to keep her cool, merely saying, "Lol.... why don't you go and find something to do?" He wandered out of the room in his dreamy way, while Pippa passed it off, explaining, "His rabbit is called Rupert – after the Children's story, you know.... He hasn't ever met a person called Rupert. "

"Children are so intuitive...." Ganga said. "He was such a dull young man....."
I wish I'd been there!

Rabbit

Ganga stays with us till July. It is a sad day when we go to the airport to see her off. Her slight lithe figure climbing the aircraft steps, she turns to wave. Lol waves back frantically. 'Why does she have to go?'

'She'll be back....' Next year.

11.

SNOOPY

Snoopy

Snoopy appeared one day and sat on the steps just at the entrance to the garden. Our dogs took no notice of him , neither welcoming nor rejecting him – which seemed odd. He was a handsome dog with a finely pointed head, and large black patches on his dense white fur. He came again the next day and sat on the step as before, sometimes closing his eyes as if he were falling asleep. None of our dogs went near him. He asked for nothing – only, perhaps, to be within sound of our voices.

It was only when the wound in his chest burst and his white fur was covered with puss and blood , that we realised he had come into the garden for help. Foreign people help dogs. We were foreign people. He had come into the garden for help, but would not ask for it. His white fur was so thick, the wound wasn't visible, and when he was closing his eyes it must have been from pain.

"Oh, poor animal!" He allowed Pippa to wash the wound, and anoint it. She tried to give him some food, but he was loathe to accept it. "No...I didn't come for that..." He had such humility. Once the wound had burst, it healed up quickly and he survived. He didn't try to join `our party', but remained on visiting terms, never expecting a welcome and was very loathe to accept any food. He was not a beggar or a cadger.

He acquired the name "Snoopy" because she would appear and disappear – he had such a quiet way of joining the company – he could have been the Perfect Spy. His modesty was exceptional. "That dog's a dark horse..." I said, mixing my metaphors, but impressed at the way he maintained his independence of us.

"Come on, Snoopy. That's for you," Pippa would say as she put down the supper dishes for the dogs. But he wouldn't come forward. "Come on , Snoopy – its yours...." At last, head down, looking shy and meek he would approach the dish. He was so slow to take up the offer, Paddy went and scoffed it first. Snoopy would not protest, and if Paddy showed any sign of wanting it, Snoopy would refuse to take it, even if Paddy had been driven off by Pippa. "What an extraordinary dog."

Snoopy and Paddy became `blood brothers'. When Snoopy came into the garden, Paddy would get up to greet him with a kiss!

Snoopy never barked or showed aggression; whereas Paddy would rush out and bark at people up the lane, especially the woman who had the effrontery to take a short cut through the garden to the Olive Grove to get down to the bus. She and her tame husband had a bit a land on which they grew vegetables. "She's probably rich as Croesus," said Pippa. "That piece of land must be worth a packet overlooking the sea like that. She'll die rich."

The dogs hated her, and we didn't like her either. She had a cunning face.

"I have my suspicions about her," Pippa said. "I believe she poisoned Dinny." (the Afghan hound she had dumped on her).

Snoopy was a pacifist. I was on the bus going to town one morning, when I spotted our Troop coming back from the garbage run. They were in the middle of the road, confronted by two big aggressive dogs who were determined not to let them pass. Paddy was bouncing up and down, barking but hadn't the courage to attack. Snoopy's reaction was to slam his tail between his legs, and hanging his head low in submission, walked straight through the barrier they presented. "You clever dog," I said to myself. "The most intelligent of them all."

One day, the other dogs were playing with Lawrence's football, chasing it round and round, trying to bite it, unable to get a grip on it when Snoopy came into garden. The sight of the ball set him off in a way nothing else had ever done. He joined in immediately – he knew exactly how to tackle it, dribbling it round the garden; picking it up, tossing it, chasing it and picking it up again – a brilliant performance. "He must have been a footballer in a previous existence," I said.

It still burns me with shame, the night I upset him so badly. It was a cold winter night. Pippa had just put down the dogs plates, when Snoopy's black and white face appeared in the panes of the garden door. Pippa let him in, and made up a plate for him. He was just about to tackle his food, when I said "That dog only comes for his supper," not meaning it unkindly. It was just an observation.

Before his lips could touch the food, he looked up at me with such a look, turned away and walked with dignity out into the cold night again. "Snoopy! Snoopy! Come back – I didn't mean it. I was only joking.... Snooooopy!" It was no good. With one backward glance to force the knife in further, he disappeared supperless into the night. He did not come back for days. It haunts me still – when will I learn to keep my big mouth shut!

We never knew his ending. He simply disappeared. I wonder what his Karma is this time? A subtle Diplomat – or a millionaire Footballer? ~~

12.

I spend more and more time with Lol, as Pippa doesn't get home till nine o'clock even on an ordinary day. I cook the supper. We don't eat till she gets back. "I've got to go away for three days," she suddenly says. "The archaeology course I'm doing to become a Hellenic guide." and heaves a sigh. Pippa only sighs when she is finding something difficult to bear. It will be the first time she has left him.

At six o'clock in the morning, as she is ready to walk out the house to catch the ferry to the Mainland. I enter by the garden door. "I'll ring you tonight," and gives another sigh as she walks resolutely out of the garden .

Suddenly I feel like the boy *who stood on the burning deck whence all but he had fled.* I have spent enormous chunks of time with Lawrence, but to be *responsible* for him for three whole days..... He is not happy to see Pippa disappear, and has no conception of time or how long three days will be, but he is brave about it. No tears, no fuss.

It is a blazing hot day. He takes his tricycle up to the space in front of the Church – the only place he can ride it where there is a flat space, He is riding it round and round in circles when Tom appears. Tom is the same age, and his mother is English too. Lawrence takes no notice of him, cycling monotonously in private abstraction.

"Law-runce! I haven't got them any more...."

"Haven't got what?" (without interest.)

"The GERMANEASELS"

"Why? Have you lost them?" still peddling abstractly in circles.

"I haven't got Them anymore." Tom repeats.

"Can't you find them? We could look for them...." still abstractedly pedaling his tricycle.

41

After playing all afternoon with Tom in the garden, he comes in saying

"I've got a headache'; is glad to have pancakes for supper, and a story in bed. I find myself *"Voyaging to The Misty City and The island of the Ever taller..."* These children's stories are much better than modern novels.

I sleep on the folding divan bed in the sitting room, which serves as a sofa during the day. This is where Pippa sleeps. He has the only proper bedroom at the end of the narrow corridor.

In the middle of the night he wakes, and shouts, "Trayzer! I want to do a pee!" By the time I get there he has done it in the potty, though aiming badly in the dark.

Day 2. In the morning he still has a headache, so we lie together on the divan in the sitting room, surrounded by the animals, dogs flopped out on the floor, the Love bird in his cage. The Budgies in theirs on the windowsill. The Hamsters trundling on their wheel in their cage – a special Hamster cage that Ganga had to bring from England. We get through the whole of "Mr. Wonka and the Chocolate Factory." His eyes have such a far away look as he listens, but the moment I stop, he says, "Go on Trayzer..." and on and on.

Now he has a fever and a stomach ache. I have no experience of children's illnesses and get a bit panicky. Athéna, a Greek neighbour, comes in to see us. She used to baby sit him when he was tiny. She says "Give him a little bit of aspirin."

He tackles a big plate of spaghetti for supper, so there can't be much wrong with him.

I think he is pining in his secret heart because Pippa is not here.

Day 3. Can it really be Day 3 ? She will be coming back tonight. Hooray!

He insists I play with his mechanical cars on the floor with him. Then I get him painting pictures. We hang them up for `Mummy to see'.

`Mummy will like them, won't she?' anxiously. He doesn't want to do anything Mummy would not like.

"Of course she will!" as we pin them up all round his bedroom.

"She will like the*m very, very much* , won't she.....?" still looking for reassurance. We are so busy we haven't noticed the dark clouds in the sky.

At 9 o'clock the telephone rings.

Pippa: "I'm stuck! The Ferries are stopped because of the weather. I can't get back till tomorrow!" a heavy sigh on the other end of the line, the only way she can express emotion. This is torture for her . She talks with him; his small slender figure in his camel dressing gown, holding the phone to his ear, "But Mummee! we've hungen things up for you...."

At six o'clock in the morning, she walks into the house with a sigh of satisfaction. He has been restless all night. He flings himself at her – the dogs do the same.

I go back down the olive grove, fall onto my bed – relieved and *exhausted.* ~~

13.

TO THE VILLAGE

We were in the garden under the tangerine trees, "This grass needs cutting – I must get Nona come to cut it."
"Your mother -in- law?"
"Yes – she loves to come. She spends the night here and does the garden with her sickle. I've got to go to the Village on Sunday – its voting day. I'll have to hire a car." Voting is compulsory in Greece.
"Why do you have to go there to vote?"
"That's where I'm registered. We lived with his family first for about 18 months."
"What was that like?" A Greek village is not like an English village.
"I *loved* it. And `Nona' , my mother in law is a sweetie – not like some.....We weren't even married then. But it didn't matter as I was Beast's Fianceé, I was accepted without any problem. 'Nona' has worked in the Olive Groves since she was a child. `Thea', her sister did the cooking for the whole family. That's how it works. Everybody had their job to do. When I was there I had to take the dinner pails to wherever they were working in the olive groves. I loved it. It was like a Hardy novel. I always loved Hardy. It was just the sort of thing I was looking for. I was only 19. The only bugbear was if you wanted to go to the Loo in the night – it was out in the yard. That was pretty ghastly...

" But we used to have a lot of fun. The family owned a taverna-cum-shop in the middle of the village. Beast and I turned it into a mini-disco. Long before we got any real disco's on the island. It was quite a new thing for the young people – it was full every

time we threw a gig. All we had was a record player – with a turntable and an arm and the speaker in the lid. Remember?"
"Yes! I had one of those. "
As we moved back toward the house, she suddenly kicked at something in the long grass. It was a bit of satin rag. "Do you know what that is?" she said. "It's the remains of my wedding dress," and gave it another kick.

On the Sunday, as we drove into the village, it was alive with people making for the voting booth at the local school house. Pippa was recognised instantly, and all manner of crones peered in at the window, yelling greetings. At the sight of Lawrence on the back seat, their hands came in through the open window to pinch his legs, screeching like banshees through toothless gums 'Psykeee moo!'""GlykÁÁ moo!" "HarrÁA moo!" "Athán-á-TEE Moo!" which roughly translated as `My Soul – my sweet one- my happiness – immortal one – "
He has been through this ordeal since babyhood, and cringed back into the seat drawing up his legs to his chin to protect himself. Visiting the village is a nightmare he will never forget.
"Oh, there's Dimitri.. 'Beast's' brother..."
He came over surprised to see her in a smart new car. "Is it yours?" with envy. "No! Rented." "Oh, Peppá! Make me a happiness....Let me drive it – just to the voting station. I learned to drive during my National Service...."
Being a good sport, she obliged. We abandoned the car and took to our feet, while Dimitri flung himself into the driving seat, to drive through the village street, stopping to greet his friends nonchalantly, getting every ounce of juice out of the experience.
"Why does he call you Peppa, instead of Pippa?"
"Pippa in Greek means a man's you know what. They can't call a girl `Penis', can they ? So they called me Peppa..." *A girl called `Penis'.*
We went up a steep alley to get to the house where a tiny woman with white kerchief on her head, black bolero over a loose white camisole, and a faded blue skirt greeted Pippa with cries of joy, "Peppá! Agapi mou!"
Once again Lawrence was pinched and crowed over. He stood it pretty well from "Nona", his other granny – his two

Grannies couldn't be more of a contrast, the slim lithe Ganga and this tiny little woman of whom it was impossible to tell her age, her body so bent from the backbreaking toil of a life-time but with the sweet nature of a child.

The house was not much to look at having had a modern bathroom built on to the terrace. What interested me was the old kitchen down in the original part of the house; the open hearth with the chimney built out over it, and the copper pans and casseroles. but now a small table top gas stove sat on the rustic handmade table, connected to a calor gas bottle on the floor.

And best of all, the storeroom filled with the old wine jars, a donkey saddle , baskets for the harvested grapes ; bags of Feta cheeses hanging on batons so the rats couldn't get at them, and the big wooden vat in which a man would press the grapes pounding them with his bare feet.

14.

THE DOG CATCHER'S CART

Bicycling back from town this morning, I saw the Dog-catcher's Cart, a cage on wheels. From time to time the Municipality round up the stray dogs. It had something in it. I stopped to look in case it was one of ours , and saw Koko sitting inside looking puzzled

"That's my dog!" I said to the man who was pushing it He said he couldn't release the dog, the only dog he had managed to catch that morning, saying I would have to come to the Police Station. I followed the cart with dread for myself as well as the dog. The last place I want to go is a Greek Police Station, but why had the dog cart been pushed up to our village? Someone must have complained that it was infested with dogs – mostly Pippa's?

I was shown into the Chief of Police's office, a pokey place where he sits, in his official capacity, behind a desk with nothing on it but a biro pen. He was not alone; the room held an assortment of `characters' of no official distinction, who could be labeled ` 'informers'.

As a female and a foreigner, I knew myself to be at a disadvantage as I struggle to explain my relationship with the dog in the cage outside. I had the same problem in the old days with *him*.....

The Chief, with a head of bovine curls, thick neck and silver buttons was not impressed. "It is *apogarevetai* (forbidden) to keep a dog *without a muzzle.*" So this was the Official line. How odd. I have never seen a dog with a muzzle on the island, and I have been here 20 years. He threatens me with court action, demanding I bring my passport to the Police station, and that somebody responsible, preferably a male of good standing should vouch for me as a female in possession of a lethal weapon – A Dog. By now my heart is in my boots.

Suddenly, one of the 'Informers' pipes up with "She's the Ingleza who was with Tassos.. pou pethané (who died). Everybody knew who was meant by this. There was only one like *him* . The situation changed instantly. In Greece, it is always *who* you know, or who knows *you*. The Chief , while remaining severe and threatening , allowed me to repossess my lethal weapon, The Dog.

When I told the others the story later, saying, "He may be in the Cemetery , but still protecting me!"

Lawrence, intrigued by `this man I had lived with...." said "Can we go and see him?" "Well..... I suppose so ," a bit taken aback, " We can bicycle there, if you like. "

He did like.

We parked our bikes outside the cemetery gates. The problem was the dogs. They had all followed us. "The Greeks believe dogs defile cemeteries. They mustn't come inside." We had to tie them to the bikes which they thought outrageous.

"Do you come here lots of times , Trayzer?"

"Not so often as I used to ...."

It suddenly strikes me that I haven't been to his grave since becoming part of Pippa's Ark

When we have to walk past a box on the path containing a skull and some thigh bones, I wonder if it was a good idea to bring him here.

"Are they real?" he asks, not a bit put off by this sort of thing. He has a practical scientific mind. From a very early age, he and his friend Toddy would go to look at the dead person on display in the Church when there was a funeral. They have open coffins at funerals. "Yes, they have to dig up the bodies after 3 years – I think – to put in the new one. It's a question of space."

Eventually I found *his* grave. I never did like it after they covered it with a slab of white marble. We stand looking down at it. It is rather neglected.

"Where you married to him?" he asks.

"No. He was married to someone else. Under the Greek law he couldn't divorce. "

"Mummy and Daddy are divorced," he says, seriously, "I wish they weren't." There is nothing I can say to that. We are silent – looking at a piece of marble with *his* name on it.

"Was he a good man?" he suddenly says. What a poser! What is the truth? "Umm....well..... I suppose you could say: `*when he was good, he was very very good, but when he was bad – he was horrid.*" This satisfies him.

As we exit the Cemetery gates, the dogs go mad at the sight of us, and drag the bikes toward us. Cycling home, he says, " We'll go tomorrow, won't we, and bring some flowers and clean it all up and make it very very nice – won't we?"

I am touched by the idea ,and glad when he has forgotten all about it by the time we get home. A grave is not *the Man.* ....

We tell Pippa when she comes home in evening , all about our excursion to the cemetery. Suddenly, Lawrence bowls me another googlie. "Which do you like best? When you were with *that person* – or now with us?"

One must reply honestly. "I am very happy as I am now.... Life moves on. " He is satisfied with this, and Pippa give a snuff in response.

She is more concerned with who it might be who got them to send the dog catcher up into the village. "I think I can guess – the woman the dogs rush out to bark at as she passes up the lane, and who sometimes takes a short cut through the garden to get down the hill. I bet it is her....I am sure it was she who poisoned Dinny and Ben. I *bet* it is her."

15.

The Survivor's handbook

He goes to the proper school now, where they make them do homework from the very beginning. Pippa sits with him at the kitchen table in the evenings, patiently encouraging him. 'Come on, Lol – you've got to do it...' while he with his blonde head hanging down, tears in his eyes, blubbers, 'I'll never be free of BLOODY HOMEWORK now!'

Lol at table writing

Since his father sent him THE S.A.S. SURVIVAL HANDBOOK, he has been studying it religiously. "Its my Very, Very Best Book, Trayzer." He still wants to have stories read to him at bedtime, but *his* reading is THE S.A.S. SURVIVAL HANDBOOK.

"We will go camping, won't we, Mummy?" becomes the eternal question. She promises that when she gets a long weekend free of her job, we will all go camping somewhere. "But it can't be before Easter, Lol. Anyway, the weather won't be warm enough before then."

"But we will go – won't we?" he persists. She promises again. Her promises are promises. Satisfied, he goes back to studying The S.A.S. SURVIVAL HANDBOOK.

"You know, Trayzer, when you join the SAS you are not you anymore."

"What do you mean you are not You?"

"You don't have the your name anymore. You're different when you belong to the S.A.S."

"You mean – you change your identity?" filled with alarm. "Is that what you want to be when you grow up?"

"They are very special, Trayzer," he says solemnly.

"But they are trained to kill people," suddenly realising that all heroes are killers, Achilles, Hector, and St. George. Does this mean that with all Pippa's dedication to bringing him up properly, with contributions from Ganga and even me.... we are raising a potential cold-blooded identity-less Killer??

We all learn interesting things from the S.A.S. Survival Handbook. How to tie knots, how to save someone from choking, how to gather water in a waterless desert, "You see, Trayzer, you take a piece of plastic sheeting and ..." And who would think that by boiling the plant Comfrey which grows in the hedges all around us, you can make a gypsum as strong as French plaster for supporting broken bones.

His passion for survival techniques – does it have something to do with being a one-parent child? His father sends him complicated mechanical toys which have to be assembled from plastic capsules and a battery operated motor, a real challenge to make it work, but he can do it. Pippa encourages him to be self-sufficient. "He's got to stand on his own two feet. What if something happens to me."

"Everybody should have the S.A.S. SURVIVAL HANDBOOK," he says. "You should get a copy, Trayzer..." ~~

16.

KOKO

Now that I've moved into the little penthouse in Effie's place next door, she doesn't mind me having Koko upstairs with me. He has learned to knock at the downstairs door loud enough for me to hear him and I go down to let him in. I encouraged him to stay in at night, but he hears other dogs in the neighbourhood shouting and wants to go out and investigate. So I am woken from my best sleep by a furtive tap on the door of the kitchen, separating him from where I sleep. I ignore it and am just dropping off again, when another tap. I persist in taking no notice – I don't want to get up, put my dressing gown on, to go down two flights of stairs at two o'clock in the morning to let him out. If anyone should hear me, they will think I've taken a lover.

A long patient interval, then another tap. In a fury I leap up, dash into the kitchen and give him a wallop, at which rolls on his back and capitulates. We both go back to our respective beds, but now every noise disturbs me. I cant sleep and long for morning. I do fall asleep, and wake at 7.30 – late for me. I go down stairs with him to let him out, and go back to bed. Half an hour later, he bangs on the door wanting to come back up. This is Too Much!

I descend like an avenging angel, open the door, stick my foot out saying "Oxó!", Greek fashion. He is shocked at this rebuff, which to him is totally unexpected. He goes away confused.

Later in the morning he tries the door again. I go down to open it, but now unsure of his reception, he is afraid to come in, even though I open the door wide saying, "Come on, Koko – Don't silly... Ellá!" No, he won't. Exasperated I go upstairs again. A little later, he knocks at the door again. I go down, open the door, to find he has knocked and run away, just like a school kid. He is sitting with his back against the wall looking sideways over his shoulder to see what kind of reception it will be. All is confusion. I have to go upstairs and get the lead to put him on it, to bring him back up. He is a very sensitive intelligent/stupid animal – just like me.

Koko is now the oldest of the dogs : 'Chairman Mao' has disappeared, and Lazarus has not been seen for ages. " Poisoned, almost certainly ,' says Pippa sadly, "sooner or later – that's the way they all go...."

Perhaps that is why she likes to have a supply of endearing animals around her so the loss of one doesn't make too much of a hole.

Being "King Koko", leads to him make a mistake. A Frenchman living in the village has a big fluffy puppy of indeterminate breed, a long haired blonde thing like an animated rug. Whenever he got the chance to escape his own confinement in Dominic's garden, he shot into ours. Paddy, Snoopy and Koko would tolerate him, so long as he kowtowed properly, which he did, though he was already as big as they were. Rolling over onto his back and putting his paws in the air he looked more like a rug than ever.

They didn't seem to notice as he grew and grew...yet still rolled over with his feet in the air – until one day he didn't. This took Koko, completely by surprise. He attempted to assert his authority, in spite of Cassy now being twice his size. When Cassy did not capitulate, Koko suddenly became aware of what he was up against with the huge hairy animal leering down on him, he turned and fled toward the safety of the house, with Cassy thundering after him. Unfortunately the kitchen door was shut. Luckily Lawrence saw the very worried Koko pressed up against the door with Cassy towering threateningly over him. Lol raced through the front door, into the house to open the garden door just enough for a very shaken Koko, to squeeze through, and keep Cassy out, then race back to slam the front door shut. Phew! A visibly embarrassed Koko never challenged Cassy again. ~~

17.

CAMPING

When Easter came round again on the carousel of the year, Pippa kept her promise to go camping. While everybody else concentrated on the Easter celebrations, we packed the little car with all the stuff we needed for two days camping. Lawrence's organising ability before we set off was impressive. "I'll do it! ...let me. I'm going to pack the car." We let him do it. Marvellous! The whole idea is to give him the pleasure of camping.

What depresses me about camping is how much paraphanelia we needed for two nights in the open. Pippa said at once, 'Well, I'm not sleeping on the hard ground. I want my mattress." It is supposed to be an escape from domesticity, I suggest.

"I don't care. I want my mattress."

So the car had two mattresses strapped to the roof held down by the hammock, ends are clamped in the car doors, plus the only tent we possessed, and all the food we needed. Paddington, and Lawrence are squashed into the back seat, Lawrence complaining that Paddy is standing all over him trying get his head out the window for air.

I'm in the front with the Hay box (for cooking) under my knees and my feet on the dashboard. "You shouldn't *do* that, Trayzer..." Lawrence says, seriously, "it hurts the car..." The car is a living organism to him.

"What do want me to do! Put my feet out the window?"

We arrive at the bay by mid-afternoon, find a superb camping site among olive trees at the back of the pebble beach. Plenty of dry kindling to make a fire. Lawrence makes an excellent fireplace of stones for our campfire. "It tells you how to in the Survival book, "he says, as if speaking of the Bible.

55

As we have only one proper tent for Pippa and Lawrence to sleep in. I have to make a bivouac tent out of an artist's collapsible easel, and two poncho raincoats. When I lost patience, Pippa took over fixing it; between us we created a first rate little tent fixed with string and pegs. Then we went for our first swim, the water cold and bracing, but the sun so hot, we could lie on the warm pebbles to dry off. Pippa falls instantly asleep.

When it came to making supper, it turned out that none of us had remembered to bring either the olive oil, or margarine for cooking, or water. We found a tap outside a villa, the water distinctly brackish makes tea taste peculiar. "We'll have to walk to the taverna in the other bay and ask for some oil," says Pippa.

At the taverna Pip and I have enormous mugs of draught lager;

"Oh, you're going to get drunk, now," says Lawrence sententiously, though he has never ever seen us drunk.

Pippa begs some oil, which is poured into an empty beer bottle to carry it back to our camp. Lawrence lights the fire. Pippa makes supper with packet soup and mixed veg. followed by apple pie (made by me).

It is lovely sitting by the camp fire as the darkness comes down, until we discover we haven't brought the hurricane lamp. "Lol! You forgot the lamp!" "No, I didn't..."

"But you were playing with it all week, and now we don't have it!"

"I thought you put it in." It was definitely Lawrence who forgot the lamp because we didn't imagine he could forget it, or the torch. I am the only one with a torch and feel smug.

We give each other points, good or bad, for having forgotten or remembered a vital piece of equipment. "I thought you were bringing the corkscrew."

"Who forgot the margarine.."

" Where's the tin opener?" Desolate moments of realisation.

Paddy is not enjoying the camping experience. Head hanging low, tail bent, he watches our activities lugubriously. "What are we doing in this place?" his whole body asks, thinking what he could be doing at home, lying in the garden, scratching. There is nothing in this cove for him. Pippa gives him half a can of dog food – very special. He has never had this before. Later he sneaks the tin into the bushes. The noise of him trying to get at the contents arouses our curiosity as to what beast it is. The light of my torch reveals Paddy whacking the tin about in the bushes .

When it is time to turn in, Paddy thinks my tent had been rigged for him, but I managed to get into it first, wriggling into my sleeping bag with all my clothes on. He curls up at the entrance with a snorting sigh.

I have never slept in a tent before. I was comfy enough, but can't say I slept. At about five o'clock I peeped out of my tent and saw a horned `Samuel Palmer' moon, just lifting up over the rim of the mountains. The promontory to the left clad with olive trees sloped down to meet the waters of the bay, lapping at the shingle, looking like oil. In the colourless light, the mainland mountains are etched in aquatint.

I hear Lol mumbling at Pippa who replies with sleepy grunts. I want to shout. 'Come and see.... don't miss this.....' For me it is the prime moment of the day, but caution prevails. Pip likes her bed. When she wakes properly, we cook eggs and fried bread. Coffee made with brackish water tastes better than tea. Paddy was lugubrious again. He stood around obviously thinking of bulging dustbin bags on his customary morning round with Snoopy. He feels deprived by this bizarre excursion, though he was given two pieces of fried bread

Getting up at dawn extends the day so much, that at 8.30 we felt it ought to be lunch time. Pippa sets about frying eggs and bread for breakfastBy nine, the sun is up; it's warm enough to lie on the beach, Pippa once more asleep on the lilo. Paddy alongside her with his mouth open, legs fully stretched. Obviously the only thing to do is to sleep away the experience.

I wandered off to disappear behind a bush; one of the problems of camping is 'performing' natural functions in the great outdoors. Paddington immediately notices I am missing, so has to look for me. Finding me squatting behind a bush, he stares in astonishment. 'What are you doing, Tray-zer', I thought only dogs do that…'

Oh, go away, Paddy.'
'No, I'll stay. I have to protect you....'
'Go away!' At this ingratitude he slopes off.

While Pippa sleeps again, Lawrence and I examined a large piece of tree trunk washed up on the shore with a remarkable bit of iron work embedded in it curved like a 'W' attached by a loop of metal driven into the trunk of the tree. 'That's like a piece of modern art, ' I say excitedly. 'It should be in the Tate. It must have been for mooring boats, or stringing nets....' Lawrence, who doesn't care about it being Art but wants something to do, says, "Lets get it out!"

So we labour at getting it out. It is hard work, having been in the tree for a century probably. At last we free it and show the trophy triumphantly to Pippa. 'What are you going to do with it?' 'I shall hang it in my kitchen.'

We have managed to miss all the Easter fuss. We have had the beach to ourselves, we might have been on a desert island. On the second day Lawrence is asking, 'Are we going home tonight?' 'No.' 'Oh, I thought we were....' The boy, bored with the long day between campfire breakfast and campfire supper. can think of half a dozen more interesting things to be doing at home now, just like Paddington.

The second night I felt cold in the early hours, and lay there wondering how you ever sleep in a tent. Just dozing off.... growl from Paddington sets every nerve tingling. Just dozing off again -Paddy leaping up suddenly runs down to the beach barking furiously, setting all my nerves on fire. Yet somehow I slept until I heard rootling sounds around our fire, but no protests from Paddy.

It was Lawrence. He had put his alarm clock on for 5. and started the fire. It was a damp morning, the sky a bit cloudy. Not a beautiful dawn like yesterday – no sign of the moon. I was glad enough to get up to the glow of the little fire.

'Do you want some porridge?' I asked him. 'Oooh yes...' We made porridge and cocoa, and sit around feeding sticks to the fire. What a jolly thing a camp fire is, those bright little flames in the chill of dawn.

Lawrence isn't so helpful in packing the car for the return home; all the stuff we have brought is just a nuisance now, and won't fit back into the car properly. There is the pile we haven't used at all, and need not have brought. There seems to be twice as much of everything..... We squash it in any old how. Now Lawrence is sleepy and irritable. Paddy wants so get his head out of the window again. In the end Lawrence has fallen asleep like a doll. Paddy, who is quite heavy, is standing on Lawrence's knee, and lying across the back of the driving seat. Pippa drives with Paddy leaning more and more heavily across her shoulders. I have the rubbish bags in my lap. 'Well, anyway,' we say to each other, ' we have a better idea now what camping means..... There must be some way to make it more simple than this.....' But we agree that it was good. ~~

18.

SOFI

When Lawrence was nine , Pippa decided he should have a male companion during the three months Summer holiday, and asked Ganga to look for a likely person in the small Welsh Border town where she lived.

So it was that Paul, 17 years old, son of the local Postman, jumped at the chance to spend a whole summer on a Mediterranean island. We liked him at once; a gentle giant, keen birdwatcher – he was just right.

It was because of Paul that we acquired Sofi. She fell in love with him at first sight and followed him back from town. " I couldn't get rid of her," he apologized. "She just *wouldn't* go away," as the silky haired red brown female gazed up at him in adoration , saying "You are my hero – I love you better than anything else in the world," and simply refused to be shooed out of the garden.

Pippa was not keen on acquiring yet another dog, let alone a female of the species. She was a pretty animal , with a delicate snout, long silky coat, and certainly not starving. It was obvious she had no intention of giving up Paul. "Hopefully when Paul goes home – she'll tire of us, and go away..."

For this reason, Pippa did not have her spayed – an expensive business, and Pippa had to bring her menagerie through the winter on what she earned in the Summer months.

Of course, that winter Sofi came on heat. Paddy and Snoopy where hard pressed as Pippa commanded them NOT TO DO ANYTHING with Sofi. Pippa had such an influence on them, making it plain she would be displeased if anything 'happened' to Sofi, they tried – *they really tried* to contain themselves. When

Pippa left the house in the morning, she shut Sofi In, and the dogs Out.

In the evenings, as the rats scampered into the roof punctually at nine to jostle for position around the warm pipe, we sat around the diesel stove reading stories to Lol. Sofi would lie stretched out on her back on the rug, showing her `everythings', paws in the air. None of us really took to Sofi. She was louche.

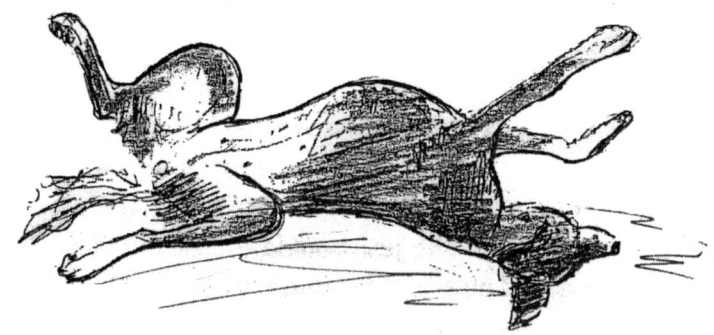

Sofi showing her everythings

Paddy and Snoopy curled themselves into tight balls as dogs do when they are very cold and tried to sleep. They were not asleep. The constant twitch of an ear, the quick opening of an eye whenever Pippa got up – perhaps to leave the room – when she didn't, their eyes shut tight again. They took a tighter turn on their bodies until they were screwed up like coiled springs.

Snoopy and Paddy curled up tight trying not to notice

When Pippa went into the kitchen to see to something on the stove, they were on their feet in a second heading toward Sofi. Pippa, returning just in time, spoke severely to them. 'Paddy! Snoopy! BAD DOGS. Don't you DARE! Brrr.... Brrr...' the growly noise she makes when they are doing something absolutely *Verboten*. Their guilt was so intense, they slunk back to the corners like defeated boxers to wait for the next round.

Came the moment when she was called to the telephone and held in conversation just too long...... when she came back into the room, Paddy was on the job, and stuck, with Lawrence trying to pull him away. 'Mummy – grab Sofi...!' Between them they tried to prize the dogs apart until Pippa had to say, 'Stop, Lol – it must be hurting them.' Paddy was looking up at her over his shoulder with anguished eyes that were saying *'I know it was wrong of me... I couldn't help it... really I couldn't...'* mortified to have disobeyed her in spite of all his efforts at self-restraint. Snoopy being Snoopy had let Paddy have the first turn anyway, and now slipped modestly through the door into the dark night, knowing this was not the place to be at the moment.

Sofi didn't give a damn either way. She was one of that sort, no sense of propriety. Her slim figure swelled. She carried her cargo with indifference, eventually delivering the load behind Lawrence's little dinghy housed for the winter in the space under the carport. Lol found them by accident when poking about in there. She had produced five. Pippa quickly got the 'English Vet' to put down three. Being Pippa, she kept two, who were soon labeled 'Picnic & Pudding'.~~

Picnic and Pudding

'Pudding' was a greedy feeder, syphoning off far more milk than 'Picnic'. He swelled up like a balloon and was soon three times the size of 'Picnic'. Pippa would pull Pudding off the teat and put tiny Picnic on it. It wasn't difficult to see which was her favourite. Pudding didn't resemble his Sire at all, but Picnic had the same long rough maroon brown hair. He would be a hairy one. It was Picnic, she took up in her hands each evening when she sat at the table. "We'll have to find a good home for the other," she said.

"But, Mummy!" Lawrence protested, "I want to keep him too...." Lawrence can't bear to part with anything. Even the old car Pippa and Beast had brought out from England years before, and when it could be repaired no more, it sat in the corner of the garden rotting. He cried when it was finally taken away. "I loved it!" he said "It was Ours..."

Pippa managed to find a good home for Pudding – not easy on an island that has not arrived at the Pet Syndrome of Social development.

Picnic , showed more and more of Paddy's characteristics – particularly in his shaggy hair, and hair colour, though he would never be the size of his Dad. He became Pippa's favourite, nursed on her lap to the blissful sensation of her tick-seeking fingernails, he believed he belonged there. When he got too big for this paradise, he still believed he belonged there, and would hurl himself into her arms. He remained a bit of a baby, never really growing up.

All the animals went through a series of names before the right one was discovered. Picnic mutated to Pickle, and finally to Picolo-Gino! as well as being 'Baggins' and 'Billie' ~~

19.

ESSENCE OF TIME

He came down to me straight after school this afternoon; Pippa was working; he hates returning to the empty house. We went up through the olive grove together so I could cook him some lunch. To our surprise we met two English tourists coming down. `Good afternoon' they said, smiling at us.

"What a silly thing to say!" Lawrence exclaimed, when they were out of earshot, "We haven't *eaten* yet." The time was 2.30.

"In English, Lol," I explain, " `after noon' means after 12 noon, whereas in Greek it is `apo-yevma' *after eating*," which is usually about 3 o'clock. I hadn't thought of this till now.

"That's *ridiculous!*" he insists and goes into a complicated Time, Space, Relativity theory of his own proving all clocks are useless and would have to be thrown away every day – "because, look here, Trayzer...' marching ahead of me through the long grasses of the olive grove, carrying his satchel balanced on one shoulder. "We... you, Trayzer... me, Lawrence.. Can't have this hour again. It's *impossible!*"

I could see how his bilingual mind analysed it. "You mean, you can have the `after eat' hour again and again, but not the `after-*noon'*, by the clock again?"

"Yes – " insisting "You would need a new clock everyday."
"So *that* means," he goes on indefatigably, "You'd have to throw away your clock and buy a new one every day because *no clock can tell the same hour again*. "

His nine-year-old mind had come to the same conclusion as the ancient philosopher – which one? Heraclitus? who said `*You can't step twice into the same river'*.

"You've hit on a Poetic truth, Lol"

"What's a *Poetic* Truth, Trayer?" puzzled
"I can't explain it – you just have to *feel* it..."
I *did* – here we were, me and him, crossing the grassy flower-filled olive grove in dappled sunlight, his red and blue T-shirt, his satchel on one shoulder....the Divine moment never to come again......~~

20.

GOING FISHING

When he is bored or in need of company, he comes down to my place. I recognise the slap of his sandals on the stairs mounting to my tiny penthouse, and the huff and puff of the dogs following him. They burst in upon me. He wants to show me his new fishing rod, his Grandpa has sent for his birthday. He takes my bathroom scales apart, and puts it back together again, with a sigh of relief. "Now I know how it works. " Then he says, "Are you doing Any Thing, Trayzer....?" I am just sitting fanning myself. "'Coz we could Do Some Thing, and take a picnic....." So we do.

We go back up to his place, put a picnic together, and then go down the steep path to the small bay below the village. "Bring your fishing rod." "Should I?" "Why not – it is for fishing, isn't it?" "But what if we catch a fish, Trayzer?" uneasy at the idea that I might insist we cook it for supper. "We can always throw it back into the sea." So he brings the rod and some bits of chicken as bait. Of course, the dogs come too.

The small bay is empty – we are both relieved at that. Beside the jetty is a whole tree trunk afloat in the water. What a thing to ride on! We can have fun with that, but being hungry we eat our picnic first. While we are eating our sandwiches, some other kids appear, swimming out to the tree trunk, leap onto it, riding it like a horse, falling off, clambering on again and paddling it with their hands. Lawrence watches them, his soul seething. With frightful passion he says, "THOSE KIDS are JUST PEOPLE!"

"What does that make us, then?"

"You're a Koala Bear, Mummy's a Koala Bear and I'm a Panda," he says with absolute conviction.

"That's better, is it?"

"Of course it is. I am going marry a Koala Bear when I grow up – because its rude to marry a girl."

When the kids had tired of the log and gone away, we got it. What a time we had with it! We played at trying to roll each other off. We lay on it, oared it right out to sea, paddling with our arms. We spent over an hour on that log, then sat on the stone jetty so he could fish, "But we won't let anybody else have the log, will we," he says possessively.

Baiting up his line with a piece of chicken he dangles over a fish hiding under the rocks by the stone jetty. Bored by waiting for the fish to bite, he leaves it and starts jumping into the water holding his nose. "You must do it too, Trayzer!"

"No! I hate getting my head under water..."

"You must!" trying to push me, but I manage to push him into the water instead. At which he bursts into tears of rage. Going back the fishing rod, he finds Paddy has eaten the chicken bits, presuming it was put there for him. He chases Paddy up the jetty. Returning to the line he finds the fish has taken the bait off the hook and gone. Outrage could go no further.

"You know WHAT THAT FISH HAS DONE – he's taken the chicken and eaten it," bursting into tears again. "BLOODY DOG! BLOODY FISH!"

He is not usually this emotional. It is very hot. ~~

He was about 10 when Pippa said, "I'm thinking of sending him to school in England. He can live with Ganga..."

"What!"

"He's got to have a proper education – the Greek won't be any use.."

`But if you send him away now, you might just as well not have had him in the first place...." It didn't make sense to me, that she, having escaped her own country, should send him back there. She didn't mention the plan again, but it stayed in the air.~~

21.

THE VILLA ROSA

Just before Christmas, Pippa said "Miss Marie has invited us to tea at the Villa Rosa." Miss Marie has the Tourist Agency where Pippa works. The Villa Rosa is a dilapidated mansion just on the edge of the town, looking like an old fashioned marble clock among the new blocks of flats on the land once belonging to the estate. The main road out of town, passes in front of the gate. What is left of the garden is overgrown and everything about the house is dilapidated and no longer functioning. The shutters have rusted and stuck, and haven't been opened for years. With only two people living in the house, there is no point in letting the daylight in.

As we stood under the frilly wrought iron canopy over the porch, Lawrence stood on tiptoe to ring the bell, which worked by pulling down a brass handle. We could hear the faint sounds tingling far off in the interior. There was a long wait, in which Lawrence speculates on how a bell `like that' works, and we wonder if Miss Marie has forgotten inviting us to Christmas tea. `There must be somebody there – Old Stavroula never goes out,' Pippa says.

Then faint calls are heard and footsteps. The door is flung wide by Miss Marie herself, tiny and stout as a pigeon, calling us `good children!', not because we are children, except Lol, but Greeks always address each other as children as if they never grow up. Behind her welcoming figure is the big hall with the mahogany staircase twisting upward like a ballerina doing a slow pirouette.. Miss Marie ushers us into the large room which serves as dining room and sitting room , a dark Venetian red room with brocade wall paper coming away from the wall in places, though it is too dark to notice it. A billiard lamp with a pink shade like a crinoline, hangs over the square dining table, illuminating the white cloth, the porcelain cups, plates of biscuits, sandwiches, cakes, bread, butter, jam and honey. All this for us? It glows like a Vuillard painting, all colour in a pool of light.

A real fire burns in the fireplace though it is not the sort of fireplace you would expect the house to have. A typically British Suburban fireplace such as you would expect to find in Upper Norwood – not on a Mediterranean island. Miss Marie, guiding us toward its warmth says proudly, `It is a *Real English* fireplace. My father ordered it from England in 1932.'

Lawrence struggles with the idea "How did it get here ?" He is a practical child.

"On a ship," says Miss Marie. She is always referred to as `Miss Marie'. It is true she never married, though she must have been a very lovely young woman. She grew up in difficult times, born during one war and a young woman in the second, the Time was out of joint for marriages. As for Children – she has hundreds – teaching them English with a real English accent just as she learned it from English Nannies and governesses. "We always had English Nannies and governesses. The British Cemetery is full of our English and Scottish Nannies..."Lawrence looks shocked.

`No! No! We didn't kill them. They died of old age within our families. They were our beloved friends." (Pippa and I suspect they taught British constipation as well as English usage.)

As we are sitting around the fire, a piece of the moulded plasterwork falls off the ceiling. Stavroula, the ancient servant – now Miss Marie's sole companion, enters from the dark doorway from the kitchen, dressed in the traditional village costume with a white kerchief pinned to the top of her head like Queen Victoria. With the same Queenly dignity , she sweeps up the plaster with a dustpan and brush. Stavroula and Miss Marie have lived in the house all their lives, one as the youngest daughter of the family, the other as the youngest servant. The only thing now, is who will die first. When Stavroula appears again, she is bearing a plate of toast , and tells us to approach the table. Tea is served.

We take our seats around the island of good things set in the pool of light in the sea of darkness. The fire is the only other point of light. Stavroula brings in the teapot and a thermos of hot water. The golden tea is poured into the delicate china cups of a design long extinct, all gold and deep blue and red – Royal Doulton? Miss Marie raises a tiny silver jug. "Do you take cream or rum in your tea?" She looks surprised when we say we prefer plain milk. "But the English always take Rum in their tea." We have to say we didn't know this. "In coffee sometimes...." I suggest, "but not tea..."

"No! No!" she insists. "In Tea. I remember very well the British Officers *always* took rum in their tea!' And talks of that thrilling time when the island was liberated by the British Army. Now you must eat." indicating the food on the table.

We wondered how to do justice to the spread. It was all for us. Pippa is always on a diet. Lawrence gets shy in company and hardly eats anything. The moment he gets home he will want a mountain of spaghetti. I try to do my best, though I haven't eaten a proper tea for years. Stavroula doesn't eat anything either, she is there to watch us eat the food she has prepared. "Eat! Eat!" they both say in the Greek way, and you *have* to do so not to give offence. It is an ordeal.

When we moved back to the fire, Lawrence needed the Loo. Miss Marie took him off to the `Downstairs' Cloakroom. When he came back he went straight to Pippa to whisper in her ear. 'What thing?' she looks puzzled. "He says there is a strange thing in the Loo. He would like to know what it is." Miss Marie is puzzled too. Curious now, we all go to see this thing. He points to an oak box with brass knobs and dials sitting on a shelf in the vestibule to the Downstairs Cloakroom.

"Oh," says Miss Marie" you mean The Wireless." Trust him to spot something technical. `A radio to you, Lol,' says Pippa quietly. He wants to know how it works, and we carry it back into the big room, where another piece of plaster has just detached from the ceiling.

"I am old enough to remember a radio as a Wireless,' I say. 'but never anything like this machine.'

"I can tell you exactly!" says Miss Marie. "This is the *very first shortwave receiver to be brought onto the island.* My father ordered it from England." just as he had done the fireplace, because British things were always to be trusted. "I remember when it arrived. I went with my father to the customs. The Wireless was all sewn up in canvass. When it was opened, the Customs impounded it immediately and sent for the Police. My father wasn't allowed to take it way. It was considered to be *the most dangerous thing* and on no account could it be introduced into a private home. It was a matter of National Security!"

We look incredulous.

"Yes! it stayed in the Customs for *a whole year* while the lawyers and police and the Government tried to work out strict rules and regulations to control its use. Wait! I still have the papers somewhere!"

Carefully sinking to her knees beside a little desk, she rummaged through the contents of a drawer. "I have it! Here it is!" she cries in triumph, waving a sheaf of papers, and raising herself with difficulty using the arm of the chair for support. "Look!" showing us the densely typed sheets in Greek script: `Five pages. 12 months of deliberation." and began translating:

"`This machine must not be used to transmit messages to the outside world. The operator must not tell other people what he has heard on the airwaves. i.e. foreign news, or give information as to currency prices on the stock exchanges.'* They were so afraid you see..." she says seriously.

We stare at the dangerous thing sitting on the table under the light, like an innocent puppy that could grow up to be a ferocious beast.

"It's ver-ry nice...isn't it..." murmurs Lawrence, touching its brass knobs with the reverence he reserves for technical things. as we contemplate this thoroughly obsolete technology, that could be a threat to government by spreading infection over the airwaves like a gas or a virus.

"They were stupid – weren't they – Mummy – to be afraid of it."

Miss Marie stuffs the five pages of regulations back into the drawer, and Pippa and Lawrence carry the Wireless back to its place in the Lavatory. Returning to the fireplace, we talk of other things. Pippa asks if Miss Marie can give us the words of the chant they sing every year at Easter.

"The Lament of the Virgin? Oh, Stavroula knows all the words. I'll call her." Stavroula enters from the outer darkness, places herself on a stool, gathering her multiple skirts about her decorously.

" Sing the Lament of the Virgin for us, Stavroula."

"Surely," replies the old woman, and begins to sing, her voice pitched in the authentic strident tones of the Byzantine Church praise, her faith and conviction shining from her like a lamp. This sound borne on the airwaves is only considered subversive by rival religions.

"And now you must sing us one of your Christmas Carols," says Miss Marie. "I love English Carols."

Pippa and I look at each other in dismay, and make stab at `God Rest Ye Merry Gentleman', manage one verse and end up helpless with shame and laughter. It's time to go.

`It's been lovely, Miss Marie. Thank you so much!"

Gathering up our coats, we leave as another piece of plaster detaches from the ceiling. Lawrence gives a longing glance toward the Downstairs Cloakroom – if only he could take `It' home ....

23.

THE EDUCATIONAL THREAT AGAIN

Now she talks of sending him to The English School in Athens. "Is there one?" "Several, as well as the American School catering for kids of diplomats and foreigners working in Greece."
"A Boarding School?" remembering how I loathed the one I was sent to.
"No... they don't take boarders."
"How would it work then?"
"I don't know yet.... I am still thinking about it," but it is obvious she had made up her mind that this is the answer, even if she doesn't know how she can make it work. Certainly he is more English than Greek; he looks Scandinavian with his blonde hair; his temperament is not Greek either.
"I'll have to go to Athens to sort it out," she says, heaving a sigh indicating the seriousness of this step.
I know she is thinking of his good in the long run, but what about her own? He is the focus of her life though she doesn't make a song and dance about it. That is not her character, but when she makes up her mind, it is irreversible.
"When would he have to go?"
"This Winter term." Gosh, I'll miss him.
She doesn't mention the idea again...

The School term begins again, when Pip is still working with the tourists all day, and the evenings as well. She often doesn't get back till 9 at night or even later. . "He's alright," she insists, "he knows how to cook himself spaghetti now." But I can't bear the idea of him coming back to an empty house, remembering that when I came home from school there was always somebody in the kitchen. So I make the effort to be there when he comes through the gate and down the garden path with his satchel on his back, dreaming of many things.

"Oh, Hullo – Trayzer!" and starts talking of the things engaging his mind. "Look, Trayzer – I want to show you something" putting a orange on the kitchen floor, "That's how the our planet looks from Space. "

We stare at it. I am filled with wonder.

Having fed him, I say, "Now I'm going home for a siesta but I'll come back."

"What time will you be back?"

"About five." He goes into his bedroom, gets his alarm clock and sets it for 5. Koko and I go off down the olive grove. He is sitting under the Nettle Tree on the edge of the garden when I lumber up the olive grove again, and immediately starts : "Trayzer... did you know that...." And on it goes. "Why ..Trayzer... would it be bad if....." "Would it be good if..." The problems of Good and Evil crop up all the bally time.

Saturday: No school. Lawrence wants to buy a special tool and piece of wood. I want wine – very necessary – and a lettuce. We ride our bikes to town early, complete our shopping. As we cycle back, seeing the kids playground is empty – he wants to stop. So we do. He insists I go on the slide. I haven't been on a slide since I was.... "Go on, Trayzer – you must!" I climb the ladder meant for tiny tots, ease myself into position and let go. I do it again, and again. This is fun! We have several goes on the slide and then the swings. I swing, remembering just how to relax the knees to encourage the swing higher and higher – I am singing at the top of my voice, happy and carefree looking up at the blue sky through the rusting autumnal leaves. The sky flashes toward me and retreats. Cars are passing on the road nearby, and I am 52 and swinging on a swing like a kid of 5! Oh, but this is Good! A marvellous experience of rediscovery – to hell with what people think.

"A BOY of ELEVEN is THE BEST COMPANY IN THE WORLD! " I shout.

"Why, Trayzer?" he asks grinning.

"Cos with a small boy you can do anything and get away with it." better than with any damn lover.... though I don't say that to him.

We went on the see-saw, then he insisted on pushing me round on the low carousel. Snoopy passing along the road recognises us, and enters the playground in his habitually cautious way. As if saying "What *are* you doing *here*?"

We don't know how he lives, he only shares some of his life with us. I haul him up onto the carousel with me. Lawrence whirls us round faster and faster. It is sickening. I shut my eyes and hold my hand over Snoopy's. He trusts me utterly and does not struggle. I know he is feeling sick. I open my eyes to a whirling scene. When I shut them I feel no movement at all yet when we stop ,I reel with giddiness

"Poor Snoopy!" hugging him, "We shouldn't have done that to you..." I apologize, but Snoopy the Outsider, Nobody's dog, licks my face with gratitude. To be held in anyone's arms is a moment of pure bliss. He has never been hugged before. ~~

25.

TO THE CAUSEWAY

She suddenly announces:"I must go to Athens to see about that school. I'll be back tomorrow night," and disappears on the first plane in the morning.

So she *is* serious about sending him away. He doesn't ask why she is going – he doesn't want to know sensing perhaps that it is something to do with him.

He is lying on the settee, I am on the settle where Nellie usually sleeps. The Hessian is torn underneath exposing the springs. The rabbit – we have a rabbit now – uses it as his burrow and keeps popping in and out of the springs. When he refuses to come out, Lawrence lifts one end of the settle and shakes it, until rabbit pops out. The hot sunlight pours in through the open front door. The mice are tucked up like pink fruit in their nests in Pippa's cupboards, while their mums raid the larder. Orange throated sexually aroused lizards flop and rustle among the flowers and dodge into and out of the stone wall, while the fruit rats munch the oranges left in the old tree. The dogs lie about panting and scratching their fleas. "What shall we do, Trayzer...." "I dunno..." thinking of a picture I might paint . "We could go fishing, Trayzer..."

"I'm tired of the bay down there -" thinking of the steep climb back up in the heat. "We don't like it when anybody else is there, do we?" He agrees. Silence.

"Tray-zer... we could take that rug Mummy wants washing to that fresh water pipe at the causeway, and wash it. Mummy would like that, wouldn't she? It would make a surprise. We could swim and I could bring my fishing rod..... "

"Okay – lets do that."

He folds up the rug and humps it along while I carry his fishing rod. Followed by all the dogs, we walk the road to the causeway which crosses the neck of the shallow lagoon, once an ancient harbour, which now accommodates the Airport runway. Planes are taking off and landing continuously just over our heads as we cross the narrow causeway to reach the fresh water pipe gushing into the sea.

"I can fish from here, can't I – there's lots of fish." Shoals of small fishes swarm about in the clear water.

"Lets swim over to the island first," I suggest, " the water's deeper and fresher out there."

"We'll come back and fish, won't we?"

We dump the carpet in the water gushing from the pipe, and then spread it over an upturned boat to dry. That done, we wade into the shallow, rather weedy water, and start swimming towards the little offshore island, with Pickle, Paddy and Nellie, and Sofi paddling indefatigably behind us, the four heads just above the water. Koko turned back to the beach, he was never a water dog.

Pickle tries to hitch a lift on my back. "Get him off me – I'll drown!"

Lawrence grabs his paws and turns him round so he has to swim in a large circle.

Fat Nellie, 'Nelly Jelly-belly', or even 'Lady Nellie Bellington', is buoyant in the water. Lawrence swims on his back, pulling her by her front legs. She loves it.

The island is a small cone with a little monastery perched on the top surrounded by pine and fir trees. Lawrence and I swim off the granite boulders which act as a barrier to save the island being washed away. The dogs forage for traces of tourist picnics. By the time we are ready to swim back, the dogs have got bored, and already half way to the beach, their four heads just above the water. We follow, and go up onto the causeway so he can use his fishing rod.

He is dismayed. "It was swarming with them before!" Now there isn't fish in sight.

I point to a crab, "Dangle the bait over that crab..." remembering as a child, catching crabs with a bit of string, a skewer and a piece of bacon. The crab grabs the bait and rides up with it. This is fun. He does it again and again. No harm to the crab who drops off smartly, scuttles to the edge and falls back into the water.

"We'll come again, won't we, Trayzer...."

"Yes – we can bring the airbed next time – easier to swim it over to the island."

Next day, repeat performance, with the airbed. He blows it up, we launch it on the water, lying across it side by side, paddling it with our feet. The dogs instantly see that this is the best way to get to the island without the labour of swimming, and try to board us. Lawrence catches Nellie, holding her round her fat body turns her into a water horse. She takes it all placidly, so long as she has his attention she is happy.

I try to do the same with Pickle but he is such a baby he pretends I am trying to drown him. Paddy goes on manfully independent, quite above these shinanigans, but Sofi, the cunning one, swims up behind Lawrence and manages to lie across the back of his legs to be transported with ease. Having reached the island, Lawrence gives Nellie a special treat by towing her around on the airbed like a dowager duchess. "Lady Nellie Bellington!" Tourists watching, laugh outright.

I shall remember these days – perhaps he will too. What better Immortality than to exist in a boy's happy memories of childhood ?

To the Causeway

We arrive home dripping with sweat. After cooking some lunch I demand a siesta. Pippa has made the garden room into a bedroom. Well, it has an old iron bedstead in it now. After an hour a voice says: "Tray-zer...are you asleep?"
"Yes."
"No, you're not – you're speaking." Blow his logical mind.
"No I'm not – I'm snoring...can't you hear?" But the game is lost. He is sitting on the end of the bed explaining how a piston engine works. "And look, Trayzer...."
So it goes on. I cook supper, read the bedtime story.... and hit the hay as soon as he is asleep. As my head hits the pillow, the night traffic of the dogs begins. I am sure they draw lots – who will want to go out next? Scratch, scratch, yap, bark. Pippa returns tomorrow night, but tomorrow is another day.
At one point I pretend to be completely frazzled. "I'm crying..." I say. He points out, "You are not really crying..." "Yes! I am. I want to Go Home." He is conciliatory. "You can go home and do your Art Stuff."
I can't leave him on his own, so we go down to my place and spend a useful hour or two polishing zinc plates for etching. He enjoys this work and is very good at it. I feel restored.

Back at the house, because I have talked about 'marbling' paper, he is intrigued and wants to do it.
"We haven't got the proper stuff up here – you need gelatine.... We'll have to try it with flour and water..." I don't really know what I am doing filling a plastic tray with water boiled up with flour, and dropping colour onto the surface, stirring it about
"We need a comb.... to stir it."
He runs off to get Pippa's comb, and stirs it through the colours. Carefully laying a piece of paper onto the surface, and pulling it off covered in a marvellous pattern. We have a wonderful time. The floor is covered with wet paper in peculiar colours when Pippa walks in. "Mumm-eeee! Do you like them, Mummy?"
She regards the pieces of wet paper all over the floor. "Interesting...." She says.

We both turn into different people in her presence. He becomes emotionally demanding and petulant, instead of the wise logical child he is with me. I become equally petulant about my nights with the dogs.

"They never do that with me," she says categorically. So the dogs are different in her presence too?

Funnily enough, we never say we have had a wonderful time. That would be giving the game away. ~~

We have supper, and I push off home while she sees him to bed and reads him a story. I can find my way through the olive grove without the aid of a torch – It is a magic place, one feels a spiritual presence – Pippa has the theory that the ancient theatre may be under steeply sloping ground.

" Think of it – they have never found the theatre – there has to be one. I'm sure its under the olive grove. After all the ancient Acropolis was up here where we are. "

Now a block of flats has been built at the bottom, fronting the road. Progress. ~~

27.

GOODBYE TO ALL THAT...

She walked out of the garden with him on Friday evening to fly to Athens, dragging him by the hand. He didn't want to go, but he didn't make a fuss. He never makes a fuss with her. He seems to know she is hard pressed. I only remember one time, when he was smaller and got all worked up about something , crying out with extraordinary passion: "That LET'S THE CAT OUT OF THE BAG. NOW I KNOW *YOU DON'T LOVE ME!*" and she, pushing him against the kitchen door, forcing him to look at her, "You KNOW that's NOT TRUE, Lol! " she always reasons with him. "You know I love you more than ANYTHING IN THE WORLD!" That's why she is denying herself, taking him to Athens to put him in that school.

"But where is he going to be – if they don't take boarders."

"I'll find something – *something* will happen...."

When her mind is made up there is no going back. She is flying by the seat of her pants again. Her father was a Battle of Britain pilot.

She will have to bring him back , I think hopefully. She *can't* just dump him in Athens like a sack of potatoes.

But two days later, she walks back through the garden gate alone.

"What have you done with him?" alarmed.

"It's all right." heaving that sigh, that tells you what she been through. "He will live with the Headmaster's Mother-in-Law," she says with confidence. That's how it has to be. "When the season ends, I'll find a flat so I can be with him in the winter. I may even find a job there... for the winter months.. to help with the expense. He'll come home for the holidays."

And that was the end of one phase and the beginning of another. ~~

Part II

Athens

The Dogs' letter to Lawrence

DEAR LORENS — IT'S ME: PAddINGTON
WE LEAD A DOG'S LIFE SINCE YOU GONE.
WE LIE IN THE GARDUN and SCRATCH OUR
FLEAS. PICKLE HAS THE MOSTEST. THEY
RUN ROUND HIS BELLY VERY FAST SO
NOBORRY CAN CATCH THEM ALL.
WE MISS YOUR PAINFUL LUVING
CUDDLES WE hope yew is learning
A LOT OF STUFF in YOUR NEW SKOOL
I AM EDUKATING PICKLE. HE IS
LEARNING FAST BUT HAS A LONG
WAY TO GO....
SOFI HAD 7 YEW-KNOW-WHAT'S
UNDER YOUR BOAT. THEY'VE GONE NOW
TRAYZER COMES EVERY DAY TO LOOK
AFTER US. WE MAKE SUCH A FUSS OF
HER. I GET HOLD OF HER SKIRT
SNOOPY PUSHES HIS HEAD BETWEEN
HER KNEES. NELLIE SHRIEK COS
IT'S DINNER TIME. PICKLE JUMPS
ON TOP OF US. WE NEARLY HAVE
HER DOWN FLAT ON HER FACE. THEN
I RACE ROUND THE GARDEN WITH MY
BACK LEGS ALL STIFF LIKE I DO
ON THE BEACH.....

WE ARE WAITING FOR THE DAY YEW KOM HOME.

SIGNED WIV A LUVING PAW

by

PADDY
PICKLE
SNOOPY
NELLIE
&
SOFI

1.

THE NEW PHASE

The moment the tourist season ends, Pippa disappears to Athens. She rang me a couple of days later, jubilant: "I've found a flat – a nice one in a block of flats in Holargos – its a good suburb and near the school. It's got spacious Saloni, hall, one bedroom, kitchen and bathroom, two balconies. I can just about manage the rent. And the great things is, Mary wants to work in Athens this winter, so she will rent the bedroom. Lol and I can sleep in the Saloni. It means she will look after Lol, when I have to come home...

That's them settled. What about me…?

As I have to come up to the house in the mornings, to let the dogs out and again at night, to feed them shut them in, I might as well spend the day up there. I can light the wood burning stove, feeding it with bits of wood I pick up in the olive grove. It's warmer than my place. I have brought up my typewriter; I can listen to the BBC World Service on her radio.

The dogs go off and do their own thing in the mornings, and come back happy to find me at home. I am glad of their companionship too, as I hardly speak to a human being, but I have marvellous conversations with the dogs – and with the mice. The cat is only one I don't care for – a ginger Tom, he can open the fridge door and pulls everything onto the floor.

In the afternoon, I lie on the settee where the sun comes in; it is really warm, no need to light the fire . The dogs lie on the floor near by. Pickle likes to jump up and lie on me, so does the rabbit. There is often conflict over my corpse, though Pickle doesn't dare go for the Rabbit. Pickle lies alongside my legs with my right hand tickling him; Rabbit lies on my chest being caressed by my left hand; she is like a hot water bottle. I stroke her gently between the ears, and down her forehead to her ever twitching nose. She will stay like this for up to an hour, sometimes nose to nose. Her teeth are serrated like a saw. I was a bit nervous she might take an exploratory bite, but instead she gives me `Chinese kisses', rubbing noses with me. When I take her out of her cage in the mornings we rub noses. If a noise disturbs her, she sits up on her back legs and stamps really hard on my chest, and then goes capering all over the room like a Mad March Hare, before landing on my chest again.

When I want to get on with other things, I put a bag of greens on the floor for her to help herself. She always goes into the bathroom to do her `pellets'. How does she know? It is much easier to sweep them up on the tiled floor.

The nights are cold and damp. I line her box with thick cardboard, and put a double thickness of old rag mats on top of the box for insulation. She is funny when I have to catch her to put her to bed. She stamps her foot and runs away. Then I crouch down and tap my hand on the floor. My hand is the hand that strokes her, and gives such pleasure. When she is lying on my chest, and I hide my hand, she will search for it. So now she comes just for that hand – giving great snorts and bronchial coughs, a combination of desire to be touched, and anger because she knows it's a trap. A woman's problem? Rabbit is the only one of the animals who hasn't got half a dozen names. She is just `Rabbit'.

The rabbit

2.

PICKLE

One night, all the dogs were home except Pickle. He and Paddington (his father) have been very thick with each other lately, going off on jaunts together – just as Lazarus used to take Koko off. (Lazarus has disappeared completely. Poisoned, I suspect.) Once Paddy and Pickle stayed away till the next afternoon. But Pickle away on his own?

"What have you done with Pickle?" I accuse Paddy, who looks furtive. I am sure he knows what has happened to Pickle. I am really worried. I won't be able to face Pippa and Lawrence if I have lost Pickle. I walk around the village – I don't know where to look dreading to find his hairy body. Poison – that woman whom the dogs hate, and who hates the dogs..... I don't trust her. The weather is dreadful – raining all the time. Where can he be?

At 8 o'clock the following evening, 24 hours after his disappearance, I heard a whimper in the dark outside the kitchen window. I rush to the front door, fling it open. A thing like a saturated sheepskin carpet springs into my arms, vibrating with emotion. He is soaked to his small skeleton, which makes him look half his normal size; he is mostly hair. Oh, I was so relieved to have him back, and hugged and hugged him.

The other dogs came forward, but did not welcome the prodigal's return, even showing a certain hostility – especially good natured Nellie. She looked quite put out. Had she been fantasizing that she would get his dinner as well as her own? Paddy, too, looked a bit put out , as if the same idea had crossed his mind.

"So much for brotherhood!!" I say, `Shame on you!' so relieved at not having to tell Pippa and Lawrence I had mislaid Pickle.

Pickle

When the weather is bad, even Snoopy opts to spend the nights inside. The dogs have a large mattress to sleep on in the porch room which opens straight into the garden. It is also the guest room.

First of all, Nellie bagged the mattress and tried to keep the others off, but when I brought in a grocery box with paper in it, she saw how warm and draught proof this could be, so she bagged it. In the day she sleeps on the high backed settle in the sitting room, dreaming of dinner time. One day I found her sleeping with her head in her empty dish waiting for the next meal. She often sleeps with one paw over her head like a night cap, and the other over her nose. Sleeping is her prime occupation.

Nellie sleeping with paws over her nose

Snoopy , that modest dignified clever animal, has created his own bed. He found a piece of dry woolen cloth somewhere. He brought it into the house together with a bit of nylon stuffing. A pile of out-of date brochures advertising Pip's Archaeological tours have been dumped in the corner for ages. Now he claws these out, spread them all over the floor for insulation, lays his own wool and nylon bits on top. None of the other dogs can think constructively like this.

Finally, having fed them and shut them all in, put rabbit in his box, I trudge off down the olive grove , and first thing in the morning trudge up again to let them out.

3.

CHRISTMAS

Entering the garden every morning, the grass dew soaked, and glistening, days full of bright low slanting sunlight – so low it shines through the cabbage leaves in the vegetables plots – even the dandelion leaves. It is warm enough for the Red Admirals, and half a dozen different species of butterfly. A Camberwell Beauty flew through the garden , and I came on two Emperor moths mating , fixed together for hours, the width of their wings something to wonder at.

Small visiting birds, Tits, Robins, Blackcaps, and Sardinian warblers, flit about. To think I was afraid of this isolation when Pippa and Lawrence disappeared to Athens . Yet I look forward to having them back.

Pippa has phoned to say Ganga is coming for Christmas. She will fly to Athens to join them, then they will come on here. I expend tremendous energy on getting the house right, such as I have never before, scrubbing , polishing the floors and the furniture, getting the beds made up. I do the garden too, and even clear the blocked drain. Nothing is beyond me, even cleaning the windows. I never do this in my own place. I dig out the Christmas tree and hang the decorations.

The animals think I have gone mad, as I threaten them with dire consequences if they undo any of my work. I must have everything right for when they come.

This is the day they are supposed come. The house is gleaming and sparkling with polish, the garden is weeded and tidy. I wait and wait all day. They do not come. No plane lands. On the News, I hear that the Airline has gone on strike. Won't they get here for Christmas after all? I hang on till 11 o'clock hoping, before shutting up the animals and making my way down through the olive grove, bitterly disappointed.

First thing in the morning I hear a plane landing. Dragging on my clothes to race up the olive grove – I pause at the sound of flying feet slapping on the steep path to my place. – the sound of a boy running – it's Lol's feet! I rush to the window – a small figure is hurtling down the path, blonde head, anorak flying. I am halfway down my stairs, when we meet with a tremendous hug. "We had to take the overnight bus, cos of the strike!" And the first thing he does is to come to find me? It doesn't come better than that.....

Later, Ganga told me confidentially, "When we were coming here on the coach, Pip said, `I'll have to chuck you and Lol out for the day, while I get the house cleaned for Christmas'. She couldn't believe her eyes when we walked in and found it looking so marvellous, with the Christmas tree decorated and everything. 'I didn't think Trayzer had it in her.....' she said."

"I didn't either! It's only because it isn't expected of me I can do it. If there is any form of obligation – I walk away."

4.

THE DEATH OF KOKO

Koko has been a bit seedy since yesterday. This evening he didn't accompany me up to Pippa's, "Aren't you coming?" He shook his head and curled himself up tighter on his rug. When I came back he had been sick – the smell was instantly recognizable as poison. Ashamed of having been sick he wanted to go out and dashed off downstairs.

Next morning – no sign of him. I went around the neighbours asking had they seen Koko. I felt wretched, realising he must have gone off as animals do when they know they are dying.... In the afternoon, a neighbour called me. "Koko is here." "Where?" "Here," (the only answer a Greek ever gives to this question.) I rushed downstairs to find Koko lying in a comatose state just inside the neighbor's front door. She is a kind little woman, a widow who has no family, so she was very fond of Koko – even to allowing him into her ground floor flat. The others would not do that.

I dashed off to find Pippa. "We must find Ann – the English Vet," she said. We went in search of Ann, the English Vet. She was having lunch, but insisted on being told Koko's symptoms. "I'll come...". Her dedication to animals was supreme.

When she examined him – he made no response. "He's too far gone... see how dehydrated he is...I'll give him a preliminary injection. Where are you going to bury him?" The only place was Pippa's garden.

"We've got to get him up there."

Lawrence was immediately practical. "We need something to carry him in...."

I had an old rug. He and I managed to get Koko onto it – suddenly the dog had become a dead weight. When he was alive, I could pick him up with a bit of an effort, now his weight was intolerable. Lawrence and I struggled up the olive grove, having to take frequent rests. As we rested yet again Lawrence suddenly said, in a deep sepulchral voice, "Before we bury him *`I want to pay my last respects."*

I looked in astonishment at the 10 year old boy whose voice hadn't broken yet. Where did the voice come from – and those words?

When we achieved the garden with our load, he set about with terrific energy digging the hole, philosophizing all the time, between the blows of his mattock, on the `Fate of All Living Things'. How did he know? He spoke is his chthonic voice which seemed to come from somewhere deep inside his body – as if something was speaking through him, or that he already knew everything he had yet to learn from life....

Strange too, was the behavior of the other dogs, who normally would have come bounding to greet us at the edge of the garden. They knew instantly something was wrong, and kept their distance. They took only one look at our group and slunk back into the house.

In giving poor Koko the final injection, Ann said, "These Corfiote mongrels are so strong, I will have to give him a dose sufficient to kill a Great Dane in England."

Even then, under her compassionate hand, his heart fluttered willfully before going out. "You see?" We have always known our dogs are special. If it were not for the poison, they would live 100 years...

We laid him in the hole on the rug we had carried him in, and covered him with an old beach towel provided by Pippa. Her garden already contains her previous animals, William, Dinny and Ben. Though Koko was `my' dog, he had his own place in her menagerie. He was one of Us. We were all deeply affected.

I realise I am going to miss him more than I know. He was part of the fabric of my existence since *he* died. I needed him those first years – his company gave me the confidence to go about. His undeserved demonstrations of affection, – nearly pushing me off my bike, or running beside me all the way to town, or coming up behind me and giving me a tremendous push in the bottom in front of the people waiting at the bus stop – people who did not see dogs as friends to man, or woman. The complaints from neighbours drove me mad in the first days until they came to accept him as charming and harmless. They even started adopting puppies themselves, but didn't know how to turn them into "Anthropi" – he was "Like a person ," they would say of him.

My next door neighbour still complained he barked at night and kept her husband awake. It made me quite neurotic. He had only to bark once and I was down the stairs calling him in.

It is all over now. I am free from further anxiety, and embarrassment – free of being cowardly – but diminished. Koko's friendship was an undeserved gift, so, fagged out with emotion and now a stranger in my own space, my tears flow for him, but the Grief is for myself. The future feels flabby again – the props we rely on without recognising them until they are taken away. At least I have Pippa and Lawrence, the other dogs, mice, rats, budgies, lovebirds, cats...

A couple of days after Koko's committal, Pippa said, "Have you seen the bone?"

"The Bone? Where?"

"On Koko's grave ....."

I went to the place under the tangerine tree. Half a cow's thigh bone, which must have been exposed to the elements for a very long time lay atop Koko's place.

We looked at each other and then at Lawrence – "Lol -did you put the bone there?" He denied it. He never lies.

"That bone certainly was not in this garden," Pippa said, "I've been clearing the garden all weekend – it wasn't in here. They must have brought it in from somewhere. I remember when Dinny died, Ben put a bone on her grave...."

What could this mean? Does a brotherhood of dogs have its own rituals for death, like the Neanderthals? Then how much must be lost by isolating them as individual pets to serve our own emotional needs?

5.
Lol's Letters

Pip stayed in Athens with him for the rest of the winter, but when the Tourist season begins she has to return home. "But he's alright – Mary's friend, Medea, has rented the bedroom. She's studying to become an actress at Drama School. She's a bit weird, but he likes eccentric people, and he's got his own friends now, two Polish boys, and Kynan is Syrian. The school is full of Diplomats children. "

"But who feeds him? "

"Medea will give him something. He can cook spaghetti for himself, and toasted sandwiches. I've made an arrangement with the little restaurant round the corner for him to go there."

"But will he, on his own?"

"If he's hungry enough, of course, he will." Subject closed.

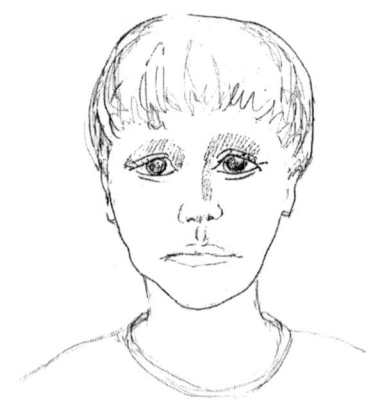

Lawrence

His letters come.

~~~~~~~~~~~~~~~~~~~~~~~~~~

Dear Mummy,

I miss you so much I cannot bear it. I can no longer look forward to going home to the flat it seems a waste of energy riding my bike back.
I did anyhow pass a very nice weekend. I went with the twins (the Polish boys) to the model airplane show at the Olympic stadium not far from school and then I went to the exhibition you told me to go to which was also very nice. It had wind surfers, camping stuff and other sports. The entry was 150 drs, but we crept past the guard and got in free. I have been trying to telephone you but you are never there it seems.

Love you so much. Love ME

Love LAWRENCE

x x x x x x x 6.02 X 10 X 23

~~~~~~~~~~~~~~~~~~~~~~~~~~

6.

Summer holidays

Time passes; suddenly the long summer holiday stretches before us: hot days, with cicadas vibrating their abdomens in the olive trees, hot nights with the whistle of the crickets. Stephen, another boy from Wales, comes to be his 'male companion' for 3 months. A short plump person, with a very agreeable nature; very clever, studying languages – German and Russian. His father is a village Postman.

Grandpa has given Lol a sailing dinghy for his birthday. Pippa has to arrange for it to be moored in the bay beside the town. When we want to use it, we have to carry the sail, the oars, rowlocks, and our picnic down the long steep hill, inevitably followed by the dogs who look reproachful at there being no room in the small boat for them, they swim doggedy in our wake. Steve takes up a good deal of its limited space, and I squat across the centre board. Lol has been having sailing lessons at the local sailing club. Sailing brings back my youth, I was brought up with boats. Bliss to hear again the hubble-bubble of the water against the side as she picks up the wind. But the wind is not a reliable source of energy in the Mediterranean, and the sun bears down so relentlessly on us, we end up diving overboard into the coolth of the transparent water, and join the dogs.

When the Summer ends, he is posted back to Athens like a parcel:

~~~~~~~~~~

Dear Mummy,

The flight over was good but I was very unhappy because I left you. I stood just inside the airoplane door and watched you – at least I think it was you because at first I could only see a hand which I thought was yours and then what looked like the whole of you. When I got into the plane a woman was sitting in my window seat, but I was too misrable to complain. That woman had "Artists Italiany" all over her bag and cloaths. She was probably a "Medea" and had high hopes for herself.

Anyway when we landed, I waited till the last person was off and the ARTIST woman had to wait too.

Please tell Granpar that I would like 2 ping-pong Match bats for Christmas if he can. And if Daddy asks say that what I realy wont is that little remote control motor for the little boat you bought me. Thank you.

I felt so bad I took those chocolate eggs to Athens and you did not have any.

<p align="center">*Love Lawrence X 60.000.000 billion times.*</p>

~~~~~~~~~~

He hasn't learned to spell in that English School

7.

ATHENS

"Why don't you stay with Lol, for a week till I can be there. He'd love it," she says.

I take the bus to Athens, and a taxi out to the suburb of Holargos curious to see how much it had developed. 20 years ago, it was chiefly made up of fields, and stone masons yards. Now the taxi drops me outside the very modern block of flats.

(How can Pip afford a flat in a neighbourhood like this?)

I press the right button, Lol's voice answers full of surprise:"TRAY-ZER!" I rumble up in the lift, though I don't trust Greek lifts. He is waiting at the gate, with a yoghurt in one hand and a spoon in the other. He leads me to a `faceless' door at the end of the corridor, opens it. "This is ours...." Suddenly, a ball of black and white fluff bounces across the marble floor to our feet. I am looking down at a tiny black and white kitten with large black eyes.

"That's Kit-Kat-Kettle," he says.

Black and white kitten Kit Kat Kettle

Kynan – that's my best friend at School – and I found these kittens on a building site. A man said we could take them. We took two each, but my other one died."

"Well, this one seems lively enough. What's that you're eating?"

"My lunch. Yoghurt and honey."

"Is that all you have for lunch?

"Yes – most days. Medea doesn't get back till late. Sometimes she brings a pizza."

He tells me about Medea. "She plays her guitar and sings in the kitchen – or sometimes in her bedroom. And sometimes her boyfriend comes, and then the place smells of his after shave."

I open the fridge door – "But there's nothing in here – except a bottle of milk. What do you eat, Lol?"

"Sometimes she cooks something, but she isn't very good at it."

How *does he survive?* "Do you go to that restaurant Pippa fixed up for you?"

"Sometimes, but it isn't very nice going there on my own. I have to be very hungry...."

"Are you hungry now?"

"Yes...."

"Okay – lets boil some spaghetti..." opening the cupboards. "There isn't any! "

"Medea doesn't do shopping...It's all right when Mummy's here...."

We go out to the nearest supermarket and stock up come back and cook.

"I'm never hungry with you Trayzer..." he says gratefully.

As I make up my bed on the divan in the hall, Lawrence gives me a dramatic account of the time when Mary came to tell Medea she had to go, that Mary wanted the bedroom back.

"Medea refused to leave, saying she is going to stay 20 years! She says she is going to buy the flat and wants to put mirrors on the ceiling... I LOVE THESE WARS BETWEEN WOMEN!!" He doesn't miss a thing, enjoying Medea's dramatics.

He still loves to be read the bedtime story. "Mummy reads to me when she comes. Medea doesn't. She knows English but can't read it."

The kitten bounces on to me , nestling against my chin as I read, then bounces off to the corner of the room and makes scratching sounds. "What's it doing?"

"It's doing a poo. I've put a tray there." I go to look. There is a very small plastic tray with a handful of earth on it, on which the kitten is performing. On the wall beside it, is an electric plug. He bends down and plugs in a night light.

"What's that for?"

"So it can see where to do it in the dark." practical as ever. "It misses otherwise."

"Oh, well, that's clever. But I think we'll go and get some Cat litter tomorrow , and find a bigger tray."

And the kitchen has an unused feel about it. "Those pots and pans haven't been used for months."

"Medea eats only biscuits and coffee when she here." he says.

I throw myself into making 21 crème caramels. He eats the lot in a day.

When Medea appears, she has those large dark eyes that never let go of you. She wanders into the kitchen, where I am cooking our supper, looking pathetic as a moody teenager. She says she is writing a film script. Asks how much it costs to make a film. "A lot," I say.

She says she wants to buy a yacht, and her own theatre. She is completely wrapped up in her fantasy life. When she gets no encouragement from me, she writes her name in the steam on the window and sighs.

Lawrence enjoys her extravagances, and she plays on it, but tonight she loses her audience when we retire to our part of the flat, to read D.K. Broster's Jacobite Trilogy. It keeps her at bay. She goes into her room to play her guitar which is abominably out of tune. "She likes it that way," he says , "it goes with her voice...." He is learning the guitar at school.

I sleep on the divan in the hall. Lol goes to school at 7 a.m. Medea sleeps till eleven. When I am not with him, I need my own space, so take myself off to a café around the corner to write letters to express my experiences, and hope she won't be there when I return.

Little Kit-Kat-Kettle is a joy. He has two boot button eyes which shine with wicked points of light. He climbs all over me, and goes to sleep on the top of my head.

Medea came back with her boyfriend the next night. They retire to her room. I decide we go out to the supermarket to stock up. When we return the place is full of the smell of nicotine, but boyfriend has gone. I don't know what he is learning at school, but he is certainly learning about life in this flat.

8.

THE FLEA MARKET

A shout of joy goes up as Pippa walks in on Saturday evening. Life becomes suddenly positive again. The next morning being Sunday, she says, "Come on – Lets go to the Sunday Flea Market at Monasteraki."

We take a bus down into the centre of Athens, under the Acropolis, where the Parthenon sits like a duck on its nest. It is a perfect Autumn day – all manner of things are laid out on the pavements, We saw three old phonographs with the trumpet like a giant lily – each one a museum piece but still working. The traders ask ridiculous prices – especially of foreigners. Pip asked the price of a plain white soup tureen such as you get in a reject shop in England. He wanted £ 30! Another old chap was trying to sell some charming mongrel puppies for £ 25 each , saying they were prime hunting dogs. Pippa walked on quickly through the gawping meandering crowd of people.

This market must have existed for thousands of years – right back to Socrates. Birds in cages, hundreds of gold finches. I hate bird in cages – my turn to walk on quickly.... There were other `attractions': A weight lifter flexing his muscles, a sword swallower going through elaborate rituals, a fire eater holding the flaming brand above his head. A muscular hairy Troll stomped around in black knickers and a leather belt with iodine stains on his bare stomach where he pushes knives into himself, and marks on his head where he cracks a nut with a stone. "What some people do for a living...." "Wait , Mummy.... I want to see...." We hung around while the man tore several packs of playing cards in half like a destructive dog. Bored, we moved on so we didn't see him stick a knife into himself, or crack a nut, which disappoints Lol.

There was another bizarre little troop of acrobats, among them a vastly pregnant girl. "She looks as if she will give birth to quinns any minute," expressing my alarm. "They'll probably make it a special feature of it and pass round the hat."

Pip bought a cat basket. "We'll need it for Kit-Kat-Kettle when we fly him home." I bought an osaka. a tiny clay gourd shaped whistle because the guy was playing Mozart on it. It sounded so sweet. Some simple instructions came with it, all for £ 1.50. I couldn't resist it – as if Mozart was in the little thing, and you only have to blow into it to bring it out.

[I never mastered it, and was heartbroken when I dropped and broke it.]

The next evening I take the overnight bus home, both glad and sorry. She will stay with him till the end of term. ~~

9.

But next time, when she had found no-one to stay in the flat with him, she looked straight at me. She knows Athens is the last place in the world I wish to spend my time –
"I've bought you a ticket...." she said.
"Oh." admiring the way she doesn't use those nauseating British formulas: *"Do you think you possibly could...."* nor does she show her relief at my acquiescence. She knew I would go with him . We don't have to waste words on polite formulas. She takes us to the airport for the early plane at 9 a.m.

Lawrence talks nonstop throughout the journey, describing all the possible disasters we could have in the air, saying "The wheels have fallen off!" which makes me caution him not to tempt Fate.
"What is Fate, Trayzer...?" *Oh, here we go again....*
"It's the thing you don't tempt...."
"What does `tempt' mean...?"
He plays me up, saying, "You *should* read this about the Life jackets. You must *know*, Trayzer."
I never read about the emergency doors or the oxygen. It tempts Fate.

At Athens airport , a long queue for the taxis; a half-hour ride to the flat, but on arrival we find the itinerant street market in full swing. I cheer up. We can buy all our vegetables and fruit for far less than it would cost at home, and the vendors are so pleasant, generously pushing another orange or handful of parsley into the bag after you've paid. I don't want to think it is twinge of conscience having rooked an innocent foreigner...?

We go to the Supermarket at the bottom of the street to stock up on other things, then I cook some lunch.

I take over the bedroom formerly rented to Mary, and Medea. Lawrence climbing up to the top cupboard discovers a lot of things. "I think they are Mary's ..." " What's there then?" "Tablecloths, sheets and these.." throwing a pair of oven gloves at me. I throw them back. We throw the oven gloves energetically at each other like a pair kids having a pillow fight. Later he says seriously, "If you were 38, would you have done that?" "Why 38?" "I don't think Mummy would have. I didn't really think you would." Pippa is 38. I am 54. What does one infer from this? Then he says, "Why didn't you have any children, Trayzer?"

"Because I DIDN'T WANT ANY!" emphatically.

"You should have had some. You would have been a housewife by now.'"

He isn't being funny, he is serious.

"What shall we do now?" The flat is such a sterile place . We are already missing the great outdoors. And we miss Kit-Kat-Kettle. Pippa didn't want to part with him. We have no animal.

"We could go for a walk, and I can wear my new roller skates."

Going round the streets with him wobbling about in the road on pair of roller skates , with cars coming at speed intent to kill, is not like being with him at home. Suddenly an innocent excursion becomes fraught with lethal possibilities . I am responsible for this child – her child. "Lol, for *goodness' Sake!*"

"What?" wondering what 'sake' is.

He takes me to a strange square plot with serried ranks of trees growing out bare dry earth. People marching diagonally through them give the weird effect of a surrealist painting.

I spot the tree house, and stupidly point it out to him. Off come the roller skates to climb up to it. It is dangerously high, much higher than his tree house at home.

"Lol – come down – its too high... Come down .Lets go and see those animals they keep in the other park." He is half way up, wondering how to proceed, so he allows himself to be persuaded. Phew!

He puts on his skates again, and we go to find the square near to the flat, where a Baboon sits in a cement cage on a

107

cement pedestal fiddling with his penis. He studiously ignores us though we speak to him politely. He has that look of an autistic person, yet with a terrible dignity. Suddenly he flashes his arse at us.

"That's rude," says Lawrence.

"He has every reason to be rude, poor thing," moving on to where a little fox is running backwards and forwards in a cramped cage next to two Peacocks trying to fan their tails in an equally confined space which has cut their feathers to ribbons.

"It makes one embarrassed to be a human being!" I say in a rage.

In the next cage, a large white cockatoo walks sideways along his perch to get closer to us. As I speak to him in a sympathetic way, he climbs laboriously up the wire of the cage until he is right in front of my face, peering at me with a little boot button eye, moving his thick black tongue against the inside of his granite like beak. Suddenly he turns himself upside-down presenting his bottom.

"He's being rude too,' says Lawrence.

"No – he isn't – he wants to show us his yellow feathers on his bottom. Look. He can only do it by turning upside-down...." As I go on cooing to him, he makes curious dipping movements holding his head upside down trying to shake his crest up for the next surprise he wants to offer us. The long yellow feathers suddenly stand up like a crown, filled with smaller softer feathers of a deep shade of primrose. He keeps turning his head to look at us over his shoulder and if to say, `There – can you see it!!' grinning with his granite beak.

"Oh, that's wonderful! Bravo!" He enjoys our praise.

A man holding a baby comes up as we leave, but the cockatoo refuses to perform for them though the man whistles encouragingly. The Cockatoo marchs solemnly back along the perch ignoring them, as if he chooses who he will perform for, and would not prostitute himself with another performance.

So these are the delights of the Great City:

10.

MABEL

Neither of us want to return to the flat, so we ramble onto an outcrop of rocky wasteland, an island of the original terrain in the middle of this growing suburb. Yellow chrysanthemum daisies burst out of the arid ground, with butterflies feeding on them. Marvellous what Nature can do. Lawrence climbs onto an abandoned bulldozer – without taking off his roller skates. A sign says they are going to make a stadium here.

Looking down I see a tiny tortoise wading over the stony ground. It looks so alone.

"Shall we take her?" he says.

"Well.... if they are going to build a stadium, she has no future here."

"She might get crushed by the bulldozers." He picks her up.

"What shall we call her?"

"Mabel," without hesitation. And so we acquired Mabel. ~~

Mabel suffered from Jet lag for a few hours having been carried up in the lift.. He feeds her by stoking her cheeks to make her open her mouth, then pushes in a bit of lettuce . She spent the night in a flower pot. In the morning, he woke her up with the heat of his hands and fed her on lettuce on the table while having his breakfast, then put her back in the vegetable rack with some dried grass.

"The sun will come in through the window and warm her up won't it," loathe to leave her while he goes to school.

Later I saw her munching well on a lettuce leaf. I put her on the balcony for exercise. She traverses the vast desert of the balcony

109

floor, devoid of vegetation with a puzzled determination. When he comes home from school, his first thought is for Mabel. He times her speed along the balcony: 1 meter in 1.34 minutes?
    We are both glad to have an animal again.

Mabel the tiny tortoise

11.

HOLLOW- GOOLI- LAND

Here in Athens it is so hot and bright, we seem to have moved straight into Summer. The sun rises like a blood red ball, balancing momentarily on the saddle of Mt. Hymettos, looking as if it will roll down on the blocks of flats below. The streets with their blocks of flats creep like a tide of pollution to the feet of mountains with the legendary names of Hymettos and Pendelis

This is a nice enough flat, but characterless in its modern functionality; a garment that never gives in to the figure wearing it. It can never be *'a home'*.

There is a generous balcony but the shutters have to be slid across the French windows against the glare which gives me a headache. I spend most of my time with the electric light on. I have never done so much housework in my life. The rooms have to be kept tidy or it looks as if a poltergeist has been at work. It can never have that sympathetic `lived-in' look.

Lol does his own washing. She bought him a plastic washing machine which he puts on the lavatory seat and it drains into the bath. But we need an ironing board…

He keeps saying "Are you happy, Trayzer? Are you liking Athens?" afraid I won't stay if I don't.

I don't like Athens but I couldn't leave him.

We have to pay the `kinoxrista', a pretty word for the tax levied on all the occupants to cover the cost of cleaning the corridors and stairways. I had to go down two floors to find Flat No. 10. and ring the bell on one of the faceless doors with a spy-hole. *Ping-pong!* The door is opened by a fat girl of 12. She knew all about the `Kinoxrista' and was very efficient at taking my money and giving the receipt. While she is doing it, I could see

111

into the flat behind her, full of posh new furniture, high gloss French polished tables, and consoles; pudgy fat settees large enough for six people, imitation Axminster rugs, and bouffant curtains over the balcony windows....

I came back up in the lift with a bourgeois matron , who quizzed me quite coldly. "You live here?" It was not neighbourly curiosity. I got the impression she thought I had infiltrated the building like a itinerant Gipsy trying to flog something. We have a camera system to scan the downstairs door when the bell rings.

"Yes," I said.

"Where?" she persisted. As I got out at the fourth floor, I pointed to our faceless door at the end of the corridor. There are three faceless doors on each landing. She went on up. I realise she occupies the flat immediately above us. I have seen her three worthless fur coats and a silver fox tippet, draped over the balcony above us. She has a pompous Petty Bureaucrat husband whose trousers are too short revealing white socks in black shoes with decorated toe-caps.

And they have an arthritic poodle. I have seen her being elaborately genial to acquaintances in the street. Well, it is obvious she regards our flat with deep suspicion. I have named her 'the Hollow-Ghoulissa'.Getting things properly identified helps me to bear it.

the Hollow-goulissa

12.

Mabel is eating well; he feeds her, stroking her cheeks. She responds to this by waving her funny legs about. She likes being handled by him, holding her by her shell, flying through the air as an airplane, and being put down on a variety of materials no mountain could have lead her to expect. She takes it all calmly in perfect trust. It's a love affair.

Even I begin to take our life with increasing calm, though tend to fly off the handle when he balances his dirty plates, not on the draining board, but on the rim dividing the two sinks.

"Don't DO THAT!"

"What?"

"Put your dirty plates there! They nearly got broken!"

"I always put them there. "

"Well, DON'T!"

"Trayzer – you're not being nice to me."

"Why should I be nice to you, when you do a stupid thing like that!"

Then he says, with astonishing honesty. "I *will try* to remember, Trayzer, but I can't be sure I will." and to mollify me, he did the washing up spontaneously off his own bat, before he went to school .

Chastened, I realise he is sensitive to my moods in a way he isn't at home. I didn't know I had so much temperament left, surprised at my tendency to exploit a situation emotionally. It is when I tire of the responsibility and the constant boring chores, but he soon gets used to me slamming about in the kitchen doing my dramatics.

"You are *so funny*, Trayzer! Oh, God, you're so FUNNY!" convulsed with laughter. It is like being `married' again. No, not that...

Mabel doesn't like to be neglected, and goes off her food if he doesn't play with her. "Come and look at this, Trayzer!" She is being whizzed about doing a loop-the-loop, then he makes her walk the plank onto the slippery plateau of the pooftee. Mabel cautiously circumnavigates the shiny leather surface stopping to peer into the void. But when he puts his hand against the side of it; she senses his hand is there, and takes a full frontal slide down the leather slope into his waiting palm. What trust! She thrives on his attentions, and gets very bored when she has to spend time in the vegetable rack.

When I was doing out my room this morning, I found Mabel behind the pooftee where she had been all night. He had had her on his chest, while lying on the floor listening to the bedtime story. He goes off into such a dream when listening to a story, he must have forgotten about her, and she wandered off. She was quite unperturbed. She is a trouble free pet, makes no mess, makes no moan. I have great respect for `Staunch Mabel'.

13.

LIFE TIME

Over supper he says, "How many years have I got to be at School?"
"Probably five?"
"Just think of all the hours that means wasted out of my life." I bite my tongue not to agree. Then, with the calculator, he works out a table to cover 25 years of living ,thus:

Altogether	Asleep
Days: 9.131.25	Hours a year : 2.922 / 1.051.200
Hours: 209.150	Hours left asleep: 73.060
Mins: 131.490.00	Mins: 4.38.3.000
Secs: 788.940.000	Secs: 262.980.000

Verdict: 33.33% of life asleep.
Awake: Hours a year: 840.075 (crossed out)
            Hours left awake: 136.100   Mins: 816.600.0
            Secs: 489.960.000

Having no head for figures, I cannot assess these calculations but I sympathize with the way he looks at things, and make him write it out in my diary.
"What about me, having to waste these hours of my life in Athens – and I don't have so many left!" I feel this quite keenly.
So he begins to work out how many days, hours, minutes seconds I have left, and concludes that I have 788.940.000 seconds , out of which I will be awake for only 489.960.000.
"My God! That's not enough time to become a Real Artist!" and start intoning:

115

Oh, Waillie Waillie up the bank/
and Waillie Waillie down the brae/
and Waillie Waille yon burnside/
where I am my True Love used to gae..."

"Was your love Gay, Trayzer?" – at which I almost choke to death. Only he can do this to me.

We end up on the roof of the flats, looking at the stars and the twinkling lights of Athens turning the ugliness into a sea of diamonds all round us.

"Have you done your homework, Lol."

"Yes – sort of.... Don't worry, Trayzer," and insists on the bedtime story. ~~

14.

THE IRONING BOARD

Today I spotted an ironing board dumped by the rubbish bins. Just what we need. Without thinking, I picked it up and carried it into the hall. The three little girls playing in the forecourt watched me with astonishment as I carried it into the lift. The fat one, followed me right to the lift and peered in. Later, I wondered if perhaps it was her mother's ironing board. They are always throwing out perfectly good things, because they are no longer the latest mode – Or was it the girl to whom I paid the `Kinokrista' that time. *Oh, dear.*

When Lol and I examine my trophy from the rubbish bin, there is something wrong with the leg. "I can fix it, Trayzer," and is happily employed for a couple of evenings which justifies `operation ironing board', but I can't forget the way that fat little girl looked at me.

He has got me playing football down in the forecourt, but before we go down, he always operates the door scanner and listens to make sure no other children are down there. I soon strained my knee and had to hobble about for a couple of days.

"I'm too old for football, Lol."

So he is teaching me chess. I am no good at that either, but he is very patient. He knows he can string me along to serve his purpose however much noise I make because of my vanity. I am sure nobody can do this job as well as I can, even if I do it badly. In this way we are welded together. I am his best bet and he knows it. On an impulse I said,` I LOVE YOU, LOL!'

"Oh, she loves me now, does she?" he remarks coolly. Blast him! It *is* like being married. Shadow boxing with the boy, brat, beast and hero in man. Dangerous – but fun.

Last night – he had been roller-skating down in the forecourt and rang me on the door phone.

"Will you come to the building site with me to get some pieces of wood and some nails.'

I went down.

It was Sunday, the building site was cordoned off by a wire fence. " We can't get in," thinking that was that.

"Really, Trayzer! You don't think this is `Old woman and small-boy- proof`, do you? adapting a phrase I often use to caution him: I don't think this is `small boy proof`, Lol.'

He found a way in and we wander the site, he picking up bits of wood and finding nails – I coveted a wooden window frame. " I could make that into a weaving loom."

"Take it, Trayzer."

"No..." Seeing I wanted it, he picked it up and carried it off the site. When we get it home, I feel I have to make the point that technically it is stealing.

"Wouldn't you have taken it?"

"No, I let you do it."

"Why?"

"Because I am a coward."

"I'm not."

"No," ending up feebly quoting ' *Don't do as I Do, Do as I Say*....'

What a lurid light falls on all one's actions and attitudes in the company of a small boy. ~~

At the weekends he talks for 48 hours – there is no respite. The varied inflections on my name "Tráyzer.... Tra-áy-zer... do you think...." "Oh, for goodness sake shut up, Lol. I'm sick of the sound of my own name!" "Why? Don't you like your name?" surprised. "I used to....not any more...." petulantly. "Okay – I'll call you Patricia," and carries on....

15.

LOSING MABEL

We are over the worse – only 14 more days to Easter and we can go home. I make a calendar of the days and pin it up in the kitchen so we can cross one off every day. "We used to do this boarding school just before the end of term."
"Didn't you like school?"
"No."
He puts Mabel on top of one of his toy cars, whizzing her about all over the marble floor. She sits there quite happily, perhaps thinking this a remarkably easy form of travel after the laborious method Nature has given her with her legs all the wrong way, shovelling along on her toenails.

He decides to make Mabel her own travelling box to take her on the plane. He finds a transparent plastic box in which he makes holes for her have air. Being Lawrence, he has to fit wheels to the box, which he does neatly and successfully. While he was making her box, he put Mabel out on the balcony for her exercise run. When he went to find her again – there was no sign of her. The balcony is large and bare, every inch of it visible, but no little domed creature was anywhere on it.

Had she managed to heave herself over the little step back into the kitchen? I had watched her trying to do this yesterday. She had looked so funny like Winnie-the-Pooh trying to get upstairs. We hunted everywhere for her, but Mabel was no where to be found. "What could have happened to her?"
"Perhaps she's fallen off the balcony – Kit-Kat-Kettle fell off."
"Really?" The flat is four floors up. "What happened?" "He was sitting outside the front door downstairs – he wasn't hurt at all."
"That tiny ball of fluff winging down is one thing, but Mabel

119

would crack like an egg." But Lawrence went off downstairs just to see if Mabel had done the same.

While he is away, I notice the partition, which divides our balcony from the neighbouring flat, has a small gap to accommodate our sliding shutter on the kitchen. I point it out to Lawrence when he returns. "Look, she might have followed the wall and she could have just got through there." "What can we do?" "We'll have to ring the bell next door and ask if we can look for her." We both dread this. "You'll have to go because you speak Greek." This time even he feels cowardly, but its the siesta time now – we can't knock them up. "We'll have to wait till six o'clock." I can see he doesn't like the idea. Nor do I, but life without Mabel will be intolerable. "We'll go together," I say, "but you'll have to do the talking."

At six o'clock we knock on the door of the neighbouring flat not knowing what to expect or how we should present ourselves as we hear shuffling footsteps and the door is opened by an old peasant woman. She must be the servant. She is mystified by our request to come in to look for a *Helona* – a tortoise on her balcony. She pulls a grotesque face. "I don't have a *'Helona'* on my balcony!" The idea is inconceivable. Lawrence tries to explain *we* have lost a tortoise which might be on her balcony. Finally she lets us in.

The balcony seems larger than ours with pots of flowers, a cupboard, a dustbin, buckets and bags. We look around, and under everything. We look and look: NO MABEL. We search again up and down the extensive balcony, he lying on his face peers under things. Nothing! We can't go on picking up things. We apologise for disturbing her. I give one last look before quitting, and suddenly see Mabel's patterned back tucked up against a flower pot among some leaves. *Eureka*! He grabs her up and carries her home in triumph. The old woman seems as mystified as before. *Xeni*! Crazy foreigners. ....Their word for foreigners sounds just like our *Zany*

Back in our place, he puts Mabel in the royal carriage he has made for her, with MABEL written on the front and a golden burgee on a mast to indicate when she is in situe like the Queen at Buckingham Palace. `Staunch Mabel' takes everything as it comes, and rides in it serenely as he whizzes her around the floor. ~~

16.

The itinerant street market comes to our street once a month like a Fair, vibrant with life and colour. It has everything – fruit, vegetables, clothing, shoes and plastics. I can't wait to get down into it.
I was looking for summer shoes, when I saw the ducklings and baby chickens. They were skittering about on a shallow topped cart like a table on wheels; tiny yellow ducklings and chicks, falling overboard and being scooped up and put back, a constant movement of golden yellow fluff with big webbed feet. The Vendor was shouting, "Yiá Paská! " (For Easter). People were buying them as Easter novelties, but these are live ducks, not toys. How many will survive? I walk away to look for summer shoes, and buy vegetables.
Returning through the market I have to pass the ducklings again – and pause. Something made me stick my hand out, immediately a duckling hopped onto it. "200 drachs the ducks- 150 for the chicks!" shouts the vendor. *That's about 60 p. Lawrence would be over the moon about it. We can take it home , together with Mabel. I must be going mad!*
The man popped my duckling into a brown paper bag, tore a couple of holes in the side for it to breathe, handed it to me as if it were half a dozen eggs. I bought a bag of meal to go with it.
My purchase bleeped all the way back to the flat. What to do with it now? I put it in a box on the balcony; in two minutes it was out of that and flapping around bleeping like an ambulance. He must want water. I plonked him a little basin of water. He stood with his feet on the bottom looking very surprised. It must be the first time he has met his natural element. He didn't respond to it all, not even to drink it. How odd. I took him out of it, and let him flap around the balcony but it was too risky, he could

121

easily have flopped over the edge. I put him in a plastic bucket too deep for him to scramble out of . It is my own reaction to our unnatural surroundings that makes me do these mad things like buying a duckling.

Duck kept up a continuous bleeping from the bucket. When Lawrence came home from school, I was surprised he didn't notice it. I was looking forward to his reaction and was disappointed. "What's that sound. Lol?" "Oh, I'm always hearing it," he says with his damnable composure. "But it seems to be coming from the balcony – there must be something out there – go and see ," busying myself making his lunch. Grudgingly he goes.

Silence. Then: "*TRA-AY-ZER*..... What is this duck doing here?" re-entering the kitchen holding it in his hands.

Lol holding duckling in his hand

"I bought it in the market this morning. They were selling them as Easter toys. I couldn't resist. Do you like it? I thought it would be a surprise Easter present for Pippa. What do you think?"

He doesn't, he is completely lost in the duck, having it on the table where it tries to eat his lunch. We soon learn that Duck has a voracious appetite.

He keeps it by him when he's doing his homework, Duck flaps around the desk; Lol's hand goes out automatically to prevent him falling off. He has Duck on his chest when we continue our reading of D.K. Broster's THE FLIGHT OF THE HERON.

Poor Mabel forgotten in the vegetable rack, mopes and goes off her food.

Only another week and we will be flying home with a tortoise, and a duck. What a circus!

Mabel in her carriage

At the Airport, I was apprehensive – surely few people travel with a Tortoise and baby Duck. The policeman watches as we hesitate putting our bags on the rollers.

"They mustn't go through the X-Ray, Lol. Ask him.."

Lawrence opens the box, to show the Policeman. Duck's head pops up immediately – the policeman smiles, takes it from him and passes it over the top of the X-Ray machine to the man on the other side. No problem. You never know with the Greeks. When you anticipate a problem, they pass it over; when you don't think you've a problem, they get all excited and turn it into one.

Duck and Mabel travelled under the seat in the airplane, Duck making ambulance noises the whole way. Pippa was there to meet us. She is expecting Mabel, but at the noises coming from the box he is carrying so carefully, she looks puzzled:

"Tortoises don't squeak!"

Driving home, she stops at a Slouvakia joint to buy our supper. While she is out of the car, Lawrence smuggles Duck out of the box into his jacket pocket. At home he gives her the box. She opens it.:

"Oh, it is only a tortoise!" surprised, until Duck's little yellow head pops out of Lol's pocket.

"OH! A duck!" staring at it in wonder and disbelief. "So small! What a Poppet!" taking it immediately into her hands. 'Poppet' is her most affectionate term for small defenceless charming creatures. To prove how small it is, Lawrence makes it stand on an orange. Pippa gets her camera and takes a photo.

The dogs are immediately alert to some strange thing being introduced into their universe. The bleeping noises make their ears twitch.

"Now Paddy, Pickle, Nellie – you've got to be nice to it," says Pippa in her sternest voice which makes them pay attention, as she places Duck on the floor. He is so tiny compared with them. Paddy puts his head forward to sniff it – Duck runs straight at him like a clockwork toy. Paddy jumps backwards knocking into Nellie and Pickle who scramble hastily into the other room, falling over each other trying to get out this alien thing's way.

"Look at it – such a tiny thing and so aggressive."

"He's not afraid at all," says Lawrence proudly.

"In the flat it couldn't bear me out of its sight, flapping after me wherever I went – he can't bear to be alone – yet look at him now, sending the dogs off."

"Where can we put him for the night?" says Pippa thoughtfully.

"In Athens he slept on a piece of newspaper under my bed."

"Yes, but we can't trust him with the dogs."

"Mummy! The Hamster cage!" The Hamsters have long since gone, but the cage remains on the top of the cupboards, a perfect safe haven for Duck.

Duck is thoroughly spoiled. He has the run of the table top at all meals. Whenever Pippa is home she has him cradled in her hands. Her hands are special , beloved by the animals, as her tick seeking tickling fingers caress their necks. Then she will get up from the table with a handful of bloated ticks to flush them down the Loo.

One night, as she was cooking dinner, she put the oven glove on the table. Duck spotted the dark hole presented by the oven glove, and crawled into it, staying happily inside for the rest of the evening, bleeping contentedly.

Now every evening he has his session in the oven glove. – substitute for his mothers warm dark underwing which he has never known. When put to bed in the hamster cage, he sleeps in the oven glove.

When Pippa and Lol were to be out all day, I took Duck down to my place, where he stayed buried in the duvet on my bed. The interesting thing is that although he is incontinent around the floors – one is constantly mopping up after him, he never shits in the oven glove nor in my duvet. He wouldn't think of shitting under his mother's wing. ~~

19.

THE 'SOMETHING' IN THE OLIVE GROVE

Coming up through the Olive grove tonight my foot struck something and I nearly fell. My feet know this path so well I don't bother with the torch, but turn it on to see what nearly brought me down. It is a wooden peg painted red hammered into the ground. This is ominous.

Coming into the kitchen where Pippa and Lol are playing a board game on the kitchen table with the Duck walking straight across the middle.

"There's *something* in the Olive Grove," I say.

"You're turn Mummy –" moving the Duck out of the way.

"There's *something* in the Olive Grove," I repeat.

Pippa catches up the peculiar note in my voice.

"What ?"

"A wooden peg painted red. I tripped over it . It is right in the middle of the grove."

She becomes alert like an animal sensing danger.

"Come on , Mummy – it's your turn."

"No, Lol, we must go and see what Trayzer's found..."

"But Mummy...."

She gets the big torch and we go out through the garden down into the olive grove where the beautiful trees grow tall as the ground slopes downwards towards the new flats on the road. We soon find the peg I tripped over, and casting about find others –

"This is bad ...." she murmurs. "I have heard rumours...."

"Why is it bad, Mummy?"

"Oh, use your head, Lol. It means they are going to build.... think of them building a block of flats in Our Olive Grove."

She has always considered it *her* olive grove, and never put fence between it and her property. The Grove is part of her space. "That's why I wanted this place – because it had all that behind it." She sighs that sigh, heavy with foreboding. " It is ominous."

We return to the house in a depressed state of mind. She cheers herself by saying, "But the Archaeologists will have to come in first. It will take time...... and who knows they might find the Theatre under there. I've always thought the Theatre could be under there. All Greek cities had a theatre but they have never found one here yet. Lets hope it is under the olive grove. It would be the most likely place. It is exactly the right situation for it."

Worse was to come.

Poor Mabel was having a boring time in a cardboard box, getting no exercise; too tiny to let loose on the kitchen floor among the feet of the dogs and, anyway, Duck has taken all the interest. You should see the way he tries to grab the dog's dinners. He goes straight for their plates, as Pippa puts them down. They back off in horror.

One afternoon, coming up to the house, and finding nobody at home, I took Mabel out into the garden to have a ramble, and experience something of real life. I put her down in the grass, expecting to see her wamble off straight away. She didn't move. She just sat there sensing the strangeness of it. I was disappointed and getting rather bored when Pippa, who had returned early, shouted to me from the house. "Trayzer – what are you *doing* out there.! You must come in!" her voice carrying an unusual note of panic.

"Its dangerous to be out there." They had just returned from town.

"I'm giving Mabel a treat, but she's doesn't seem to be enjoying it."

"Come in – you *must* come inside!"

Pippa isn't usually this worked up. Picking up Mabel I came back into the house as a light rain is beginning to fall.

"They say its worse in the rain."

"What is?"

"There's been an accident at a Nuclear Power Station in Russia – The Radio-active cloud is spreading out all over the place – over us as well..." Going off to close the windows all over the house.
  Oh, Great. He and I have to return to Athens tomorrow. ~~

20.

On the way to the airport with Duck, and Mabel, Pippa stops for a baby Blue-tit, sitting in the middle of the road, opening and shutting it's mouth. Lawrence jumps out, the Baby Blue-tit is added to our travelling menagerie. Waiting for the plane to come in, we sit at a table trying to push some grains of Ducks fodder into the Baby Blue-tit's gaping beak, and take turns carrying Duck to the Ladies or the Gents to give him a splash in the washbasin. The Blue-tit survived the journey but was dead in the morning. It saddened me to have to put his pretty body in the trash bag.

We have brought the Hamster cage with us for Duck. From our balcony I see that the grass has been mown on the roundabout. I go down with plastic bag to gather it up for the Duck's bedding in the hamster cage. Perfect.

Lawrence coming in from School, looks at the grass.

"Tra-ay- zer...." cautiously, ".....they told us at School not to sit on the grass, or to touch it with our hands."

"Why?"

"Because of the radio-active fall-out." I had forgotten about the invisible threat in my desire to make the Duck comfortable with a product of Nature.

"and they say you should leave your shoes outside, and wash your clothes everyday ... and your hair...."

What a time to be responsible for somebody else's child, a duck and a tortoise! "So much for Man's scientific genius if this is where it gets us! Okay then I'll wash the grass, and you can wash the Duck."

He takes DuckaDuck off to the bathroom to dunk him in the washbasin.

"Don`t wash Mabel! She might drown!"

"Don`t panic, Trayzer," he says calmly," She's armour plated, it probably won't affect her.

There is panic buying in the supermarkets. Announcements saying no more than ten tins of evaporated milk per customer. Fresh milk is banned, though you can still get it. What to make of it?

Ganga has telephoned Pippa saying we should take one drop of iodine a day as a safeguard against thyroid cancer. But you can't get tincture of iodine in Greece, only the stuff in tubes. Frankly, I am rather glad of that.

When over supper, I get dramatic "Lol – you've been born onto a polluted planet!"

He is philosophical.

"I know Trayzer. It doesn't matter. We all going to die anyway."

In the midst of all this mess, the Duck is the sweetest reality. Perfect in shape; a pleasure to watch at all times. And marble floors are perfect for incontinent Ducks. He sleeps on a piece of newspaper under my bed. He has to be in the same room with me and is quite content so long as I am near him. He nestles in a rug, tweeting continuously and trying to put his beak under the stump of unformed wing. But the moment I walk out of the room, he springs up in desperate alarm, and flings himself after me bleeping like an ambulance, feet flapping on the marble . If I am lying on the bed reading, he will stay contentedly bleeping for hours.

Lawrence is determined that Duck shall swim. Ducks and water go together don`t they? But Duck has an aversion to water. Lawrence fills the washbasin and puts him in, his down soaks up the water, and he sinks, whereupon he panics. Lawrence has to take him out.

"But it's extraordinary – a Duck that sinks? On a river they start swimming from birth, they have to."

"You know what it is, Trayzer," logical as ever, " They must get oil from the mother's feathers. He doesn't have a mother so he hasn't got any."

"He's just beginning to get some real feathers. Look at the tufts on his cheeks, and they are growing underneath him – where his boat shaped body would be in the water."

"He'll be alright when his own oil glands begin working.... he has to swim sometime." as we watch the very angry ducklet standing on the bar of soap shaking himself and trying to get himself clean and comfortable after that abominable bathing session he is given every evening. To him it is entirely unnecessary. His ocean is the marble floor where his big flat feet go flap-flap-flap, and he does his rectal rejections as copiously as he would in water. I spend all day cleaning up behind him. Thank goodness for marble floors.

Duck loves the bedtime story, Lawrence nursing him on his chest lying on the floor while I read the next book of the Jacobite Trilogy.
   "You know something, Lol. He's going to be a very literary Duck."
   "What does lit-errary mean?"
   "Likes a good story, like you do. Okay! that's it for tonight, Ducks!" closing the book with a snap.
   "No! No! You can't stop there. I won't sleep!" giving a disgraceful performance of bullying.
   "Lol! It's 10 o'clock and I've got a headache!"
   "You MUST Go On!!" It's like struggling with a Boa Constrictor.
   "No! That's *it* for tonight. Put Duck in his cage and GO To Bed."

He obeys, taking Duck-a-Duck-Do-Duck as he calls him, to the Hamster cage, immitating Duck's rectal ejections like Punk music. Phuuu-arttt! He (or is it a she?) is now called ""Duck-a-Duck-Do-*Dat*" because he always does that.
   "Oh, for goodness sake, Lol! I have that all day..."

Duck shitting

21.

The problem is: *What to do at the Weekends*.....
To escape the cage of the flat we go over the Zoo area in the centre of a nearby square, where the big monkey sits on his concrete plinth staring into the distance. The fox they had last winter has gone – it ran constantly around its cage. " One can only hope it escaped somehow. When you think how many wild foxes there are in the suburbs of London."
"Are there ?" he asks.
"Yes, I've seen two big ones crossing the road in Surbiton in the dark. Felicity in Wiltshire has them visiting her garden. She puts out food for them." His eyes go dreamy with the thought of a fox in the garden.
Wandering through the streets on a Saturday afternoon we come to where the blocks of flats suddenly stop, and the mountain begins. A goat path beside the road leads straight up the mountain.
This is the mountain we see from our balcony, hanging in the air above the flat roofs where the television masts bristle like whiskers. We never thought it was attainable.
"We could go up there, Trayzer..... It's Sunday tomorrow."
I hesitate, unsure how I would manage, never having climbed a mountain.
"Shall we , Trayzer?"
"Okay, we'll make an early start before it gets hot."

I had no suitable shoes, and borrow a pair of his trainers, which seem all right. We got up really early, before it was light. We took with us a backpack of provisions, plus his SAS Survival kit which includes oiled string, upholstery needles for sewing up wounds, Disperin and Elastoplast; plastic bags for collecting water, a fishing line and hooks.

"Are there likely to be any fish up there, Lol?"

He explains with some wit, that the kit has everything for survival in woods, deserts, and mountains – but not for survival in Athens.

It took just twenty minutes to get from the flat to the edge of the mountain, then the upward plod began . I was pleased with my performance. We got up to the saddle by 7.30 am. in 1½ hours. I didn't know I had it in me!

We lay in the sun with the insects and butterflies all around us – a fascinating variety of insect life. His SAS magnifying glass is very useful in the absence of my reading glasses. I hadn't thought there would be so much to read on a mountain.

Below us lay the ugly sprawl of Athens, like a dirty cubes of sugar. We discuss Man's ruination of his one true resource, this planet. Lol doesn't need to have it pointed out to him. He knows. We both loathe Athens, the artificiality of it. It is not me influencing him. He influences me far more than I do him. So we lay like puppies against our mother's flank. I had my coffee in a thermos, and we ate some of our picnic. We still had the whole morning before us, so we climbed higher to the next saddle. At the very top is the Radio station and Radar post. In fact, you can drive a car right up to the top but we had the satisfaction of doing it the hard way.

At noon, it was hot so we started to descend. That's when the nightmare began for me. My feet in his old trainers had no support and no grip on the loose stones and shale. I dithered at a snail's pace. It seemed so much farther going down than coming up. Fortunately I had thought to pick up a stick. Seeing me having difficulty, he told me to put my hands on his shoulders. With great patience, he led me down the mountain like the blind Edipus. How compassionate of him, and how demoralizing for me.

"Oh what an awful thing it is to be old!" I cried.

"What do you know about it, Trayzer?" His gallantry takes my breath away.

"Oh, say that to all the old women you know, and you will be a Prince of Men!"

"What does that mean, Trayzer?" is all his reply.

Back in the barren territory of the flat we look up at the mountain from the balcony knowing that there is another world within our reach – we have been there !

"We will go again, won't we, Trayzer ?"

"Yes! But I must find some proper shoes....I'll go into Athens tomorrow."

22.

DUCKY

Ducks are much more intelligent than chickens. There is a dignity, even pomposity, about a duck which a chicken doesn't have. We still don't know if Duck-a-duck is male or female. He loves to have his back stroked, and his chest tickled, and stands up tall to receive it. He responds by gently nibbling our fingers. No wonder we use the term "Isn't he a duck," and "Ducky" as a term of endearment. You need to keep a duck in intimate circumstances to retrieve the endearments of one's own language. I suppose in the olden days they lived so intimately with their animals......

So long as one of us is near by, he stays peaceful for hours. He loves the bedtime story.

Duck-a-Duck made a hint of quack today. He enjoys his bath in the kitchen sink now, swimming about and splashing himself until he is wet all over. Lawrence had to warm the water before he put duck in it or Duck would scream "What are you doing to me! " struggling and flapping.. He seems to be able to produce oil for his feathers. He doesn't sink anymore and doesn't seem to mind cold water now.

Yet the demands of an incontinent duck are pretty excessive. He will not feed unless I stand over him , holding out strings of spaghetti. I wonder at those literary females who write novels as well as having a husband and five children. One duck might prove too much for them.

23.

HOLLOW GHOOLIE LAND

Had to pay the house tax again, The Kinoxrista. We had a note pushed under the door about the election of a new "Secretary of the flats" – it sounds Orwellian to me. Now we must pay the kinoxrista to 5th floor. I feared it might be the "Hollow-goulissa" herself. I had got used to going down to the 2nd floor where the fat girl of 12 dealt with it.

I ring the ping-pong on the faceless door on the 5th Orofos. A woman in her late thirties flings open the door,and gapes at me. There behind her is an identical interior to the one two floors down. The effect on me is of a "Kafkaesque" nightmare. The idea that behind these blank doors with the spy holes are identical interiors with the characterless characteristics of success.

I offer the money and the piece of paper. She calls her husband, who has the built-in self-importance of an under manager of an insurance company. A photograph of him as a young man in air force uniform sits in a silver frame on the console immediately opposite the front door. Is this some kind of deterrent? If so against what? Adultery or burglary? One can see this is a childless household; both work in order to have the `good things of life' i.e. complete sterility. I miss the fat girl of 12, she is real and has potential. ~~

These Athenian blocks of quality flats in a good area, each with its elected body of vigilantes exuding an invisible moral gas on the staircases gives the feeling that Big Brother is watching us.

This morning when Lawrence opened the door to go out, I saw a figure in the corridor and shot back into the kitchen.

"Tray-zer....what's the matter?" coming back inside to understand my reaction.

"That thing out there!"

"Its only the cleaner....."

Is this paranoia all my own, or is there some basis of truth in it? Perhaps it is because we are `foreigners'. It makes me aware of my own spots and returns me almost to my wild condition. They talk of the `anonymity' of city life. Is it so?

The other day, one of the female vigilantes who was about to enter the lift in the hall, heard my footsteps on the stairs and significantly waited to see who it was coming down the stairs. By not using the lift I was behaving furtively. No one in their Greek mind uses the stairs if there is a lift, whereas one of my phobias is to be trapped in a Greek lift in an earth tremor, or a failure of the electricity. Anyway, walking the stairs is better exercise. They should do it more.

Lawrence pretends he doesn't care, but he is as furtive as I am about avoiding confrontation with this unseen force. He listens on the tele-device to the front door – if there is no sound, he is prepared to go down to play softball. So it is not just me. It teaches me what it must be like to be Black, or Asian, or Jewish in a white ghetto. This is a pseudo middle-class white ghetto. There are no black people unless they are diplomats.

This morning we breakfasted at dawn on the balcony with Orion on high – so what is there to complain about? Nature is alright. It is everything else that is wrong. Suddenly he said, "Trayzer – if the people upstairs were to dangle a rotten pig over our balcony... what would you do....." He knows my weaknesses.

"I would complain to Pippa, saying Do you Really expect me to put up with this sort of thing?"

"And if you couldn't complain to Mummy..." he went on relentlessly.

"I would sit and hold my nose, I expect. What would you do?"

"I would call the police."

Why can't I think like that?

He comes into my room. The invasion of my personal space is difficult for me. It is an invisible area but a child can walk right through it like a veil.

"Ah you asleep, Trayzer?"
"Yes," I say hopefully.
"Would you like to play chess?"
"I'm too stupid to play chess."
"You have to be intelligent, Trayzer, to know you're stupid."

24.

It's his birthday. I buy a sponge based fruit tart – a commercial no-cook assembly job – but it looked impressive with extra cream and the candles. He was surprised and pleased by it. If only Pippa were here. He has presents from all the family, of course.

I gave him a small Cretan dagger I found in a souvenir shop. It had something inscribed in Greek on the blade which he managed to translate.

I am a Cretan knife
Full of honour and stature
But I am also a reminder
Of really truthful friendship.

I was impressed by the poetry of this, and the careful way he translated it, crossing out his first effort: `honest friendship' to substitute `really truthful friendship', which I think characterizes the relationship existing between Pippa, Lawrence and myself.

25.

UP THE AIRY MOUNTAIN

Sunday: we go up the mountain again, making better time by half an hour. This mountain quickly gets you into shape. I have my "Puma Magic" shoes now. People jog up and down this mountain on Saturday and Sunday mornings, so we get up very early to be up on the saddle by 7 am, without having to share the path with anyone puffing up or down it.

The sky begins to lighten as we near the rim of the saddle – the little pine tree by the rock marking the levelling off. We find an old shepherd's Bivouac , a circle of dry-stone walling giving protection from the wind. Here we drink Ovaltine and eat hard boiled eggs. I make a sketch of the sun coming up. Then lying on my back watch the Swifts. It is so quiet. We hear some voices shouting but they do not materialize. After the early morning joggers – that's it. The mountain belongs to us.

This time we went on to the next higher peak, crossing the asphalt road leading up to the radio station. Here there are picnic tables. Suddenly he gives an hilarious demonstration of the sort of people who would use these picnic tables having driven up in their cars with children ,who run around and scream, while the parents scream at them "not to run" "Not to fall". Every time the child comes near enough, the mother stuffs its faces with the picnic fare of cold macaroni in tomato sauce.

"Oh, stop, Lol, if I laugh anymore I won't get to the top."

On the next steep bit, he says, "How many sandwiches have we got?"

The answer is `not enough', so we curtail our climb and sit on a rock dangling our legs over Athens, fully visible below as a bacteria of concrete crawling over the space between the high hills with the classic names, and the ships steaming away from

Pireaus as funny little wedges on the flat surface of the sea. We discuss the many deep and critical issues facing mankind.

"What if an earthquake struck now, and it all disappeared into a big hole?" he said.

"I think we would be a bit worried – with so little picnic left."

We descend again to the Bivouac where he starts building up the broken walls and planning the future. "Tray-zer..... we could sleep up here....we could bring up more water and make soup...."

"Water is the heaviest thing to carry," I protest. "and what would we sleep in? We haven't got a tent or sleeping bags... at the moment the sun is hot, but it will be cold up here at night."

"In my S.A.S. Book it says you can retain your body heat in a dustbin bag......"

"For a start you'd need a pretty big dustbin bag.... Come on, we'd better start on the way down."

On the way down we met an ancient tortoise who did not retract at our approach and allowed Lawrence to stroke his head.

In my `Puma Magic' shoes I manage the descent with ease. "We are goats!" I say triumphantly. In the twelve hours we spent on the mountain, we saw only about ten people in the distance jogging. "Ten people out of 4½ million. Not bad."

"The 4½ million are the sheep," he replies.

In the evening he makes a barbecue on the balcony – sitting in a howling wind cooking four small souvlakia and some sausages, while the duck, shut inside, rushes about the windows, looking for every possible exit to the balcony. It is a greedy thing. ~~

Duck running

25.

To vary the boredom I feel in the streets, I walked a different way to the Bank. And discovered a row of small old dwellings – the only sort of dwellings that used to be in the area. My heart warms at the sight of these cottages surrounded by a wilderness of garden. I pass one run down place of two storeys built after the war? It must have been a desert here then. On the posts of the pergola naked dolls are tacked up, and old Teddy bears. It looks like a witch's dwelling; these dolls are to ward off the Evil Eye.

A fat old woman was lying on a swing seat which must have come off a tip, (The Nouveau Riche society quickly jettisons its `pragmata' the moment it is unfashionable), it had a bit of uncovered foam rubber for a mattress. The old Biddy lay there gently rocking herself by pushing with a stick against a table, to and fro, to and fro. I embraced the idea of her joyfully. After all she had everything – a house , a garden and a swing seat in the poshest suburb of Athens! Rocking herself to and fro over a freehold fortune, probably living off a government pension. The thought of her cured my depression.

Then at the check out of the super market I was standing behind what was an English woman and her small son. This desirable suburb is full of Embassy people. He been to the Greek Church with the other children in his class, and had taken communion.

"They made us drink blood."

"It isn't real blood, darling, its wine," she assured him. "It symbolizes the blood of Christ, That's all."

"They gave us Blood."

"It wasn't real blood, darling,"

"It was Horrible."

Back in the kitchen waiting for him to come home, surrounded by tiled surfaces of blue circles on cream, I could howl like those poor creatures in the Zoo; the disdainful monkey, the little fox, the peacock who can't raise his tail – they are *me!*

But it is alright once he walks in the door. Cooking supper, we hurl epithets at each other: OLD BEAN....OLD FRUIT He coins "OLD-DRIED-UP-BIT-OF-PUMPER<u>NICKET</u>!"

"Ouch! that draws blood, Lol!" and tell him about the boy in the Supermarket convinced he had been drinking blood which leads to our making up a science fiction story about the "Hypothetical UFOtimis" who, banished from earth for their frightful deeds, return from space like rampant teenagers to raid the supermarkets of the things denied them Out There. i.e. Hamburgers in packets and frozen chips, and make up this song:

Hairy Tokes with magenta ties
Proboscical hooks and elliptical eyes
Who bare their chests and wear no vests-
Who prance and trance ,retreat, advance
With poltik spear and brutik blade
A bash their spoons like frictik goons
To the bulbous light of Galactic Moons. ~~

He was kicked on the toe at football and is hobbling. To rest the foot he lies on the bed beside me, playing the guitar – exploring sounds rather than playing.

"Oh, listen to this, Trayzer...!" as he discovered a sequence of sounds that delight him. I am jealous of him learning the guitar. "I was taught piano, but I can't play it now – I could read music once. What is the use of being taught anything."

We try to play the guitar between us as if we had only one arm each, he pressing the notes and me plucking the strings, like driving a car with someone else changing the gears. The absurd things we do, makes up for everything else.

26.

Sunday morning we climbed the mountain by moonlight. A full moon on its way down, as the sun was coming up; an experience I associate with Greece as I have only had this experience here.

We ascended with far greater ease that last week, making the ascent in silence. Below us, Athens twinkling like a sea of candles – the quiet of the sprawling sleeping city. That it can ever be that quiet is astonishing. It always seems to me that the early hours of the morning 4 a.m., are the least evil time, as if evil has been exhausted temporarily. So I feel no fear setting out in the early morning.

We don't speak until we reach the saddle, with the light in the East just beginning; then he begins to pipe like bird. It is cool, but not cold at the Bivouac. We have our ovaltine which, at that hour and place, tastes like the nectar of the Gods. Then the sun came up as a great red ball with the full moon facing it from the west. I have really taken to this low altitude mountain climbing.

He sets about making himself a bed in the Bivouac.

"In books," I suggest, "you often read about people sleeping on pine needles. I've always wondered what that would be like." He takes up this idea immediately. There are plenty of Pine trees around. He comes back with armfuls of sweet scented pine needles and makes two comfortable beds for us to lie on. We both love the early morning and having the mountain to ourselves. Once the joggers start panting up the slopes, it is another place. So by 8.am. we were ready to descend again. He can think of half a dozen things he can do back at the flat, like making a book case out some planks we got from a wood store.

On the way down he says "Give me a subject, I'll make up a tune." He did. The tunes varied with interesting rhythms though he is not interested in music. Then he wanted me to whistle.

"I can't whistle," I say.

"Yes, you can – do it like this."

"My lips are too dry. I haven't been able to whistle for years."

"Trayzer! You're so feeble. You won't help yourself." which touches a nerve I thought was dead. My mother saying "You give up too easily..." and School reports "Must try harder..."

"Oh, shut up, Lol – You make me think of School."

Then he wants me to tell him about my school days. There is nothing worth remembering about my school days, but he insists, so I drag out "Bice", our Headmistress as awesome as a Roman Senator, and our nun-like existence at a Select Girls Boarding School in Surrey, England. "Didn't you have any men teachers?"

"Men! Good God no! No man was allowed to cross the door, except for two ancient gardeners and the Archbishop. We had only dried out Spinsters."

"What's a Spinster?"

"A woman who doesn't marry."

"You are a Spinster, then."

"Yes, and No. Its a type you rarely find these days."

"Didn't you play tricks on April Fools Day? We do..."

"No."

"Weren't you ever naughty? What was the worst that could happen to you?"

I find myself saying *"To be sent to ring the front door bell...."* and then trying to convey the Awe-fullness of the procedure which led directly to the Headmistress herself, and she, by the very nature of the introduction knew you had committed an 'unmentionable awfulness or crime.' "Like what?"

"Well, there was one girl – it was after I left the School – who was caught writing graffiti in the Loo......"

"Everybody does that."

"Not then, and not us. We didn't know what to write. We knew nothing, never discussed it – weren't even curious...."

(*What kind of a Dinosaur am I? Its only 40 years ago, not a century*).
"Anyway that girl was *precocious*. I don't know where she learned her stuff, but she was expelled and immediately married a Peer of the Realm and became "Lady something..."

"I like those stories so much," he says, as we arrive back at the asphalt road. I cannot think why they should appeal, but he is interested in everything odd.

Walking through the blocks of flats, shops and cafes. We stop by the flower shop to talk to the Grey Parrot, who looks at us thoughtfully, listening to my crooning, and replies in words we just could not quite catch as in a dream. He was very polite.

"If only we could catch what he was saying – it looked as if he had just had a Great Thought."

"One time Mummy and me stopped by him, he shouted "*Malaka!*" (a very rude word).

"Well, he is obviously in a benign mood today. He is certainly the only bit of `wild life' on Mt. Hymettos." The only wild life we have encountered on the mountain has been a tortoise, a speckled toad and a mosquito that got into Lawrence's ear. ~~

27.

This life we lead in Athens feels like wartime to me. I am a Wartime child, but this is being at war with my surroundings in the depths of my psyche. hating this concrete environment, where the trees grow through holes in the pavement. At least they have their roots in the earth beneath. I wish I had such a hole to get my toes into.

I roam the supermarkets like `Ophelia distract' – or is it Perdita. *Here's Rosemary and Rue… Here's Hamburgers and frozen chips.* I get less and less responsive to the contents of the shelves. I walk back through the dismal little park in the middle of the square where the big monkey, eyes close together, long nose and quite fleshy jowls is sitting on his box staring at nothing . I give him a fatuous `*Good morning.* It is a long time before he turns his head to look me up and down in complete contempt. I get the message: *Humans are the lowest form of life.*

Back in the flat it feels like house arrest, whereas at home I live like a hermit and feel free.

Cooking the supper, I started singing old songs like `*Keep right on to the end of the road'*, `*When this blooming war is over…Oh, how happy I shall be.!"* He is fascinated.

"Go on, Trayzer – sing another."

`*Pack up your troubles in your old kit bag, and Smile – Smile – Smile. While you've a Lucifer to light your fag…..'*

"`What's a Lucifer?"

"A match – the un-safety sort with a pink tip, called Swan Matches."

"Sing it again, Trayzer. Don't you know <u>all</u> the words?"

"I wasn't born in *that* War, you newt! I was your age in the <u>Second</u> World War which didn't have such good songs, and used the old ones again."

"In the next war they won't have any songs, Trayzer.."
He *knows* that....?

Ever since reading in his `Bible': The SAS Survival Handbook, that a plastic bag can retain body heat, he wants to try it. "You can survive on a real mountain in a plastic bag, Trayzer..."
"That's daft. How can one sleep in a plastic bag?" thinking of the Super Market bags we put the rubbish in.
Coming back from school one day, he produces four large orange municipal plastic bin bags such as are draped over the handles of the Street cleaner's handcart.
"How did you get hold of them.?"
"I pinched them while the chap wasn't looking."
"That's *stealing*, Lol," feeling I have to make the moral point.
"They don't care – they can always get more."
"They're still too small to sleep in, Lol." hopefully.
"I'll make them work," he says.
After he has done his homework, he sets about adapting the plastic bags, by cutting a hole for the neck, and two holes for arms and demonstrates, by lying on the floor, how he intends we should wear them, putting head and arms through the one bag, and pulling the other up over our legs like a sack. "You see, Trayzer – it will work."
Now the prospect of spending a night on a bare mountain is staring me in the face. ~~

27.

NIGHT ON A BARE MOUNTAIN

It takes the whole week to get our act together assembling everything we will need for a night on the mountain. I choose my wardrobe with care. Pippa's winter clothes are in the cupboard, a sheepskin jacket – and a pair of Pip's ski-tights under my track suit trousers, a light weight wool jersey, a woolly hat and gloves.

Lawrence puts his faith entirely in the rubbish bags, wears jeans, shirt and jersey only.

"It may be hot by day, LOL, but it will be cold up there in the night time, ..."

"Never mind, Trayzer," his mantra.

We set out after supper about 8.30 pm. walking though the streets until we reached the edge of the mountain where the asphalt ends and the rocks and scrub begin. We know all the paths now, used by the joggers and early morning health freaks. But what kind of freaks are we?

I have brought my torch, I don't want to break my neck. When I switch it on, he says, "Don't shine that near me – it will spoil my night vision!"

I quickly discover it *is* better without the torch.

We made the ascent at a slow and steady pace. Three quarters of the way up we can tell how far to the summit by the sound of the wind.

"Its awfully windy up there, Lol...."

He agrees to stop at the first good spot before we get to the top. We find a place under a pine tree and a thicket of Arbutus. The proximity of the pine tree is protective and sympathetic, making lovely patterns against the dark sky – for the dark is light enough when you are in it. We drink some cocoa I have brought in a flask, shuffle into our plastic bin bags, extra large, and hope for the best.

The dustbin bags did nothing for my body heat, with three rocks sticking in my back. I thought I was going into an uncontrollable rigor. I discovered that if I lay on my left side I was cold. If I lay on my back, I felt warmer; if I lay on my right side curled up, I was much warmer. After what seems like eternity, I look at my watch. 11.30! *The night is long that never sees the day....* What misery! A bit later, his voice is saying:

"Trayzer.... are you awake?"

"Yes!..." viciously.

"What time is it?"

I struggle to read my watch with the torch. "2.30."

He gets out of his bag to walk up and down. He *is* cold. So much for municipal dustbin bags. He gets back into his bag. The wind gusts like an express train passing over us.

Half an hour later, "What time is it, Trayzer?" And so on till 4.30.

Sick of lying in a plastic sleeping bag I suggest we start walking up to the top as the exercise would warm us. We get to the Bivouac, settling ourselves gratefully into it, make tea and soup, in his billy-can on the little camping stove which takes costly solid pellets. It took a hell of long time , the pellets having to be replenished constantly.

Impatient for my cup of *instant* soup. "Hardly a survival technique." I remark petulantly. "What do they do on Everest?"

By this time the dawn made a smudge of lurid pink across the East. Then the sun came up magnificently – materializing in the sky above a low bank of cloud , making everything worthwhile. `Wow!'

By 7 a.m ,the wind still gusting, and having finished all our provisions we are ready to make the descent. Stopping by a stone where people had engraved initials and signs the way people do, he wants to add a skull and cross bones. I suggest if he wants to make a statement he should put "Save the Environment – or something effective like that."

He spends a long time chipping it into the chalk. "How do you spell `environment?"

"Put `Earth' instead." wishing I had thought of something shorter, suddenly appreciating the economy of the four letter words. Obscenities are shorter.

By now the health enthusiasts are chuntering up the slope in their tracksuits, gasping out a "Kalimerá" as they pass. As we were already half way down, they probably thought – seeing me – `poor old thing, she can't get any higher.'

"They don't know we have been here *all night*," proud of my achievement.

"One never knows what one can do until one has done it and survived.

NOT BAD FOR A DRIED UP BIT OF Old PUMPERNICKIT!"~~

28.

THE BIKE

Dear Mummy,

I have not been doing anything about my bike. Do you think you could put some money from mine to Trayzer's account so I could get it, because I do not know how mach I may need for buying it. So wait till I tell you. Wring me back please soon. There is not mach news. I will have my physics exam on tuesday and Trayzer says we will be back in 17 days.

Are the small black flees starting to crawl along the wall yet? (does he mean Ticks? T)

Duck laid its first egg (Nonsense! T.) He is very well and tonight he will sleep with Trayzer but tomorrow night with me.

Love x 6.000.000.000 XXXXXXXXXXXXXXXXX

[His spelling hasn't improved.]

Pippa has sent the money for his racing bike. We have to go down into Athens to get it on the last Saturday before going home. For him it is a mystical experience, but it wasn't a mystical experience when no taxi driver would take us *and* it. We stood in the road flagging down taxis. They stopped readily enough, but when we indicated the bike, they made the Oriental negative, raising their eyes and making a little 'tchuck' sound. How on earth were we to get it back to Hollow-ghooli-land?

152

Suddenly a man who had been watching us, signalled to us, indicating his tiny truck. (called here a `Tricky-tracker') How much? 1.500 dracs – more expensive than a taxi but not unreasonable if we were ever to get the bike back to the flat. He lifted the new bike carefully into the open back, with Lawrence watching that he tied it in safely. The three of us squashed into the driver's capsule – a tight fit, with Lol in the middle – we `tricky-trackered' all the way back to Holargos.

Lol brought the bike up in the lift. As we entered the flat, we could hear Duck-a-Duck. He was standing in the middle of my bedroom floor, upright with outrage at having been left alone for so long. What a whigging he gave us. I had to stroke his breast to calm him down. The interesting thing was that Duck had made no messes. He was constipated with indignation. When we leave him overnight to go up the mountain, he is tucked in his blanket asleep and does'nt notice our absence. But this desertion in daylight, had him really stirred up.

To celebrate the Racing Bike, we decide to go out to have a Pizza. The bike had to come too, maneuvering it into the lift again, and we had to have it beside our table on the pavement while we ate the pizza. A boy with a new bike – a dream union, probably sex in later life will hardly compete with this dreamy rapture.

"I'm going to ride it round the block, Trayzer..." and with elegant movements of his long strong legs, he disappears out of sight. I walk back alone to comfort Duck, and anxiously await the sound of the lift bringing up boy and bike ~~

29.

We are through! We hope to get off the ground tonight with the Duck, the tortoise, a sprouting avocado, a guitar and my typewriter. Pippa rang to say a friend would pick the bicycle up and bring it in his car. We would never have got a taxi to take it.

I've cleaned the flat, washed and ironed the sheets. As an Artist I have no talent for domestic chores, especially a shitting duck. Though I don't regret Duck; Duck has been a beautiful experience. I couldn't have got through these weeks without the wisdom of the boy, the beauty of the duck and the calmness of the tortoise. I am the only one to fly off the handle.

Looking out over the balcony I see tiers upon tiers of women's lives pegging out washing, beating carpets, loving, worrying and waiting for *them* to walk through the door demanding to be fed. To every balcony a woman's life.

We have just discovered that the old woman next door where Mabel blundered, is all alone. Her relatives visit her once a month. I saw a man and a woman going in there one day, greeting her with *'Yasu, Manna'* so must have been her son. They looked prosperous and successful, but obviously they don't want her living in, bought the flat as an investment and stuck her in it. A simple village woman living in the vacuum of an Athenian flat – no more sitting on the doorstep chatting with her neighbours of an evening……..

I hope to God with get out of here tonight.

We did! It was raining cats and dogs in a freak storm, the water in the streets spraying up to the windows of the taxi taking us to the Airport. We had nine items of baggage. Mabel in her travelling box, as serene as ever. Lol put Duck into his blue zip bag, with a plastic bag inside 'in case he shits'.

"He won't shit, he never does in a place where he sleeps, though he might get rather hot in a plastic bag," I suggest.

'Never mind, Trayzer." dismissing my British foresight.

At the Check-in, an American girl behind us is delighted at Duck's head poking out of the zip bag. "Oh, look! A real Duck!"

Duck in bag

The girl behind the desk checking us in, smiled too and said, "You must pay for it."

I thought she was joking until she handed me our ticket slip with 'One Duck Alive, 2 Kiloes ' written in the box marked VOID. Finding the right desk and queuing again took time. We were charged 80p for this trouble. By the time we were free again, it was 9.45pm. Our flight was for 10.30, and I insisted we go through into departures. The duck was very hot, thrusting his head out of the hole make by the sip, beak open gasping.

155

He had to be thrust back in again, his indignation palpable. Lawrence wanted a toasted sandwich, "They don't do them in the departure Lounge, Trayzer…" and was fed up. So was I. I had thought of everything, in the way I had learned from Ganga. And produced a packet of biscuits, some fruit juice, and processed cheese which he sat and ate in sulky silence, while I gave the indignant duck a drink of water. Duck was being admired with curiosity. A young father brought his child over to look at it. The child cried when he was taken away.

Finally the flight is called, we climb into the bus clutching Duck in the zip bag, Mabel's box in a carrier bag, my typewriter and radio, his guitar, and struggle to our seats on the plane. By now Duck is frantic. Lol has it on the flap down table in front of him. "Shall I let him out of the bag?"

He does so. Duck stands up tall, shakes himself and turning round on the little table, shits copiously into my lap! But I had thought of everything… and produced a roll of kitchen paper, mopped up my denim skirt.

"You said he wouldn't shit in the bag!" Lawrence laughing his head off, his sulk quite gone.

"If he'd shat on you, you wouldn't be laughing." Yet I was never so grateful to have received the whole lot in my lap – except for a tiny drop splashing onto the trousers of the young man next to me who was also amused and didn't complain.

When the plane took off, Duck back in his bag under the seat, settled down giving no trouble. 40 minutes later we were down on the ground with Pippa there to meet us.

Waiting for the baggage to come up, Lol let Duck out onto the floor, where he stalked about waggling his tale in ruffled dignity, and shitting copiously as usual. People amused and bemused as we mopped up after him with the kitchen roll. Only 'Zany' foreigners do this. Lol took him off to the washroom to give him bath and dry him under the hand drier.

So we arrive, home and glad to be so – with our zoological lives intact.

30.

BACK HOME

Back in my own pad, sitting on the terrace 9.15 in the morning, no chores. I don't do chores...... I can pursue my thoughts as far as I like without interruption....Oh, this is the Life!

Then I hear the flap of sandals like the Duck's feet coming down the path , and up the stairs to my door.

"*Tray*-zer – . We're going to take the duck swimming. Do you want to come? "

The irresistible invitation.

It's Pippa's day off, – she doesn't get many. We pile in the little car, to drive to her favourite bit of rocky coastline. Duck in a open work basket so he can see what's going on, is serene and doesn't make any mess though we have brought plenty of kitchen role.

But he is surprised when Lawrence puts him on the water. Suddenly Duck is literally *in his element!* plunging his head in, he flings the water over himself and swims off flicking his tail, with us following, seeing him quite differently as he bobs along at eye level.

Lol swimming with duck

Later he dries himself on the rocks and does his preening, and ends up sitting on Pippa's bum as she lies on her stomach reading her book. She can read for hours on the rocks in the hottest sun.

He is on his own much of the time during the long summer holidays. Pippa is working, taking tourists to the archaelogical sites.

He is happy enough with the animals for company, and he is always making something, or taking something apart and putting it back together again. If he wants company he comes to find me.

One afternoon, "*Tray-* zer ....will you come? Paddy tried to attack me...."

"What!" The idea of Paddy attacking Lawrence is unthinkable.

"He ran at me as if he was going to bite me. I fired my catapult at him... I didn't want to....." shaken by the experience . "I think he is sick. Pickle too. I've shut Pickle in the bathroom. Their coats are all wet..."

It sounds like the poison again. I grab up some rubber gloves, remembering my mother going into the kitchen to give the dog a bromide when it was having a fit.

No sign of Paddy up at the house,

"He was there....." pointing to the place, "But when I went towards him, he rushed at me and chased me all down here. He wasn't like Paddy anymore. That's why I fired my catapult at him..." Still feeling guilty. We search the garden, the lane and olive grove, and ask the neighbours, but of Paddy, there is no trace.

I took a look in the bathroom and see Pickle standing in the middle of the floor looking as if a bucket of water had been thrown over him, his thick ragged hair drenched in sweat.

I am not much good at these crises, relying on Pippa to see us out difficulties, but she won't be back till nightfall. "We must get a Vet quickly...."

I have to ring the only Vet I know, who knows me because of *him*. It is the middle of the hot siesta hour. "I'll come for *you*," he says. (*He* has his uses still ..…)

The Vet. gives Pickle an injection. "He should be alright." Miraculously, by the time Pippa returned about 10 p.m. Pickle looked as if nothing had happened to him. He is her favourite, – her baby.

"It's that woman again....."

Pippa is a very fair minded person, and non-judgmental but she has lost all her animals this way.

"She is a Witch!" said Lawrence passionately, mortified by his guilt at having fired his catapult at Paddy, in his distress.

"You couldn't help it, Lol – it must have been horrible to see him like that."

We are very sad. That's Koko, Snoopy and Paddy – all gone. At least we've still got Pickle.... and Nelly-Jelly Belly... and of course, Sofi.

We never did find Paddy – so he never got a bone on his grave.

31.

Lol and I went to town to hire a 'Tricky-tracker' to take his small dinghy down to the Bay. We walked down the hill to catch the bus, accompanied by the dogs. We got on, paid our fares and sat down. Suddenly there was Pickle beside us on the bus. I stuffed him under my skirt. Dogs are not allowed on the bus. We got off in town, ignoring Pickle who slid off behind us like a shadow. Nobody had noticed him. What Relief! It would have put the bus in an uproar.

Having found a willing 'Tricky-tracker', Lawrence lifted Pickle into the open back. To onlookers, it must have looked if we had engaged a pick-up truck to transport one dangerous dog back home. We stuffed ourselves in with the driver and off we went.

Up at the house, we struggle to get the little boat out of the garden, and onto the back of the truck, plus the mast, oars, boom, sail and ropes. We make the short journey down to the Bay, and into the water, and pushed off.

Grueling hot, with no wind, the boat is like a small frying pan under a hot grill. I have to crouch beside the centre board to avoid the boom. Never mind, it is only a short distance we round to little bay below the house . We tie up to the stone jetty, and plunge into the water. Lol diving in again and again from the jetty, while I swim in lazy pleasurable circles in the sea as clear as gin. Then he wants to row by himself "to see how fast I can go..." and shoves off , rowing at furious speed, and returns full of enthusiasm

"You try now , Trayzer – it's SO NICE!"

I take the oars as I haven't done for 40 years, it all comes back so easily. I shoot away rowing backwards in Time a batty old woman whizzing about in a small boy's boat – watched by the Greek grandmothers whose only recreation is cooking, curiosity and condemnation.

"What a lovely Nautical Day!" bringing it backing to shore. shout..

"What's naughty about it?" puzzled,

We dismantle the mast and boom, and rowed about between the moored boats.

"There is nothing, simply nothing quite like messing about in boats... " I yell, with a wet dog in my lap who is licking my face.

We set about packing up. He wants to leave everything under the boat, rather than drag it all up the hill again, but a man watching us recommends we take it away, or it would be stolen. Carrying the mast, the oars and the boom, the sail and a length of rope between us, we set off. At the bottom of the long steep hill, he has a bright idea to support the oars and the mast, boom and oars on both our shoulders and hang the bag in between. So we proceed like Safari bearers bringing home the Wildebeast up the quarter mile of hill.

After which I am cudgeled into playing table tennis, as well as cooking the supper. It is 11 p.m. before Pippa gets home from a long day with the tourists to be greeted with his ecstatic, 'MUMM-EEE!' throwing himself at her.

As I pick my way home through the olive grove, I wonder who has the wonderful gift of him. She who made him having all the mental, and financial anxiety of Love, whereas I who never wanted children, have all the fun.

Lol sailing dinghy followed by the dogs

32.

THE OLIVE GROVE

I got a shock when I came up through the olive grove this morning, to find a trench has been dug. A bulldozer has barged in from the top of the grove, where there was only a footpath. I had to clamber down into the pit and up the other side to get to Pippa's garden. Lol and the dogs came back with me to see the pit. "Look at that line of bones....."

There was a long thin strata which seemed to be made up of small bones. "I wonder what that could be..."

Later, we were rummaging about in the storage area under the carport, where he wants to make a work place when suddenly we hear Pippa calling, "Lol? Where are you?" She's supposed to be at work.

"Here," the traditional Greek answer. "Is Trayzer there?"

"Yes."

"Why doesn't she answer...."

I detect something in her voice as if she has been physically hurt or shocked. She is usually so calm and collected. We crawl out of the carport to find her standing on the terrace by the font door with her arms clamped across her chest – a sure sign of distress with her.

"We've got to leave this place!"

"What? Mummy, I want..... " following his own line indefatigably.

"Forget about what you want for a moment. There is something more serious. We must leave this place."

"What do you mean? "

"Sell this house. Go and live somewhere else!"

"W-h--y?"

"They are going to build *in the Olive grove* . They are going to build two blocks flats in the Olive Grove. Panayoti has just told me. We can't stay *here. Lol.*"

"What?" he is still baffled.

My stomach has gone cold at the idea of them leaving this place, not being at the top of the olive grove any more. What will I do? "Yes – they have bulldozed a trench…" speaking at last. "I had to climb my way out of it coming up this morning...."

"But Mummee...," he insists, "we can make a fence...."

"I am <u>not</u> going to live behind a fence, Lol. If I had wanted a fence I would have put one years ago. *I don't like fences.*"

The Olive Grove has been part of her from the first. "We *have* to move." She is adamant.

"But Mum – meeee.....it won't be the same...."

"Sometimes you *have to change for things to stay the same.* I must get back to town...."

She marches out of the garden. We listen to car driving off. Her mind is made up.

She is calmer in the evening . We take the lantern to go and look into the trench to see if there are signs of anything archaeological that might stop them building, but there is only the seam of bird bones. "They must have eaten lots of little birds...."

"I am sure the Theatre is under here – they must dig deeper if they are to find something. Think of the slope it is on, and the centuries of earth washed down over it by the rain. but I expect somebody has `*Messon!...*" she says bitterly......

Messon – the word implies *somebody who knows somebody who knows somebody in a position of power......*

[*`I don't think they play at all fairly, Alice began,*
in rather a complaining tone,
and they don't seem to have any rules in particular;
at least, if there are, nobody attends to them.']

"Anyway the moment the Summer ends," she says, "I must start looking for another place..... but I've good news for you, Trayzer, – you won't have to go back with him this time. There is a couple from South Africa – he teaches at the school. They will live in the flat rent free but will look after him. They have a child of their own. It should work out alright...."

I hope so.... recognising the end of one phase and the beginning of another........... but I don't like to think of him living with strangers......

Part III
KORAKIANA

1.
Pippa finds her place

I spend most of the day up at the house, loving these days as much as I hated the days in Athens. The miracle of the world has returned with the inner peace, the absence of distraction ,or responsibility. My eyes have switched on their infra red beams. They see again, penetrating the make-up of colours, watching butterflies. They are not just lamps to prevent one falling down holes in the street. It is almost like being under the influence of a drug – though I never have. I don't need it. Each day takes on its own distinct individuality made up of little things; the dew is still glistening with spiders webs hung among the bushes in galaxies of inverted umbrellas – as large as a foot in diameter, with smaller inverted umbrellas above and below . I counted 29. The dew made each one visible – a little planetary system in dew spangled orbit.

Lumbering up the now mutilated Olive Grove carrying a lump of wood over my shoulder for the stove, I am surprised to see two `town' women and their children above me, one of them waving her hands about in an expansive way, saying – `Our land goes right down to there...` pointing over the extent of what used to be the beautiful olive grove which now looks like a First World War battleground.

As I plough on doggedly up the path which leads to Pippa's, I have to pass them. They freeze into silence at my appearance – obviously not a native, carrying a piece of wood over my shoulder like a peasant. I greet them politely with a `Kalimera', to which they do not respond. I know what their minds are making of me and that I am trespassing through the house of their dreams.

The car was parked at the top of the grove, where the bulldozers have forced an entrance. This lovely winter afternoon she said to her friend whom she wishes to impress and fill with envy "Let's go and see my piece of land,' and they piled the children into the car. Ten years ago she would not have had a car, or known how to drive it.

As I walked doggedly on, clambering over the ruined ground to get to Pip's garden, I could feel their cold eyes on my back seeing me as the intruder, whereas I see them as the intruders. They could not guess the curses I was inventing. I was cursing her to hell for her pride in a piece of beauty her beautiful dream would destroy; remembering that the bee orchids grow just there, and never will anymore trapped beneath her ugly pretentious villa.

A day later, as I take the path again, I come to the fence posts and two days later the wire fence has gone up. She must have told her husband that night..

Now I must go round the edge to the track that leads to the church and approach Pip's place by the lane. Fortunately, there must always be a way for the faithful to get up to the church.

Once the season is over, Pippa loses no time in looking for a new place to live. Every Sunday we go house hunting around the villages within commuting distance to the town. She doesn't want anything modern or new. When somebody has the temerity to suggest that `surely a flat in town would be the more practical. " she spits. "I can't live in a flat! What would I do with the animals!" Animals have been an essential part of her life since childhood "the dirtier and most impossible, the better..." she says, and doesn't deny that she prefers animals to people. "You know where you are with animals."

"I fancy that village up there....." Driving towards it through the olive groves, the village appears sprawled on a ledge half way up the mountain "Isn't it a bit far out?" "Its only 20 mins from town by car."

Pippa goes up and down the alleyways like a truffle hound. The Villagers, once they understand what the `foreigners' are looking for, lead us off in all directions to show us ruined dwellings, that haven't been inhabited for 50 or more years. No toilets, no bathrooms – such things hadn't existed when these houses were lived in. After the War, the Greeks went off to seek their fortunes in America, Australia, Germany – there was nothing to do on the island except raise sheep, goats and pick the olives. The people who were left relied on the money sent by their relatives working abroad.

Just before Christmas, as we struggle down a rough path between ruined cow byres – our village guide indicates a canopied porch to a large village house.

"The back half of that house is for sale," he says, "Old Fotios lives in the front. An `Ingleza' lived there for two winters. *Kyria* Rhoda who owns the back half wants to sell it."

Glancing at the house, Pippa shook her head. "There 's no time to look at it now – we have to meet Ganga at the airport."

Ganga is coming for Christmas.

A week later, Pippa said, "I want to go and look at that house before Mother goes back." Which house? Hadn't we looked at all the ruins.

"That house on the path at the top of the village," she firmly says. "I've contacted *Kyria* Rhoda who owns it. She is waiting for us...." Rhoda is `Rosie' in English.

As we drove into the village, *Kyria* Rhoda was looking out for us – a sturdy village woman with very few teeth in a passionately ready smile. In her fist she waved a key as big as a Church key – the key to the house.

We followed her up the steep path to the canopied porch of the house Pippa had seemed to dismiss when we were here before. Rosie thrust the key into the ancient lock; it worked with a grinding sound then she gave the double oak door a shove with her shoulder and we found ourselves in a plain room with wooden floor; a box staircase leading upstairs. A narrow corridor with two dismal bedrooms on one side led out of the `Saloni', to the kitchen where a vast hooded chimney bosomed out of the wall; below it, the bare hearthstone, where they would have hung a cauldron over a fire of sticks or charcoal. There was also a bread oven in the wall, (every house had to have its bread oven). The kitchen door lead into another canopied porch with steps down into the narrow alleyway.

In the sitting room, the narrow wooden stairway went up to an empty spacious landing with a tiny bedroom partitioned off it. The Greeks are such outdoor people, they have little idea of how to use interior space. Lawrence was hopping around looking at things in his own way while Rhoda was chattering on about the `Ingleza' who had rented the house two winters ago.

"She had a *Bathroom* put in!" *Kyria* Rhoda cackled, as if a *Bathroom* was a huge joke.

"I born in this house.... 15 brothers and sisters. ... we `go' on the mountain!" but adding in a solemn tone, of course, she had a *bathroom* in her own house now, at the other end of the village.... not wanting us to think she was not `modern'.

"Where is the bathroom?" Pippa asked. We had not seen a bathroom. *Kyria* Rhoda, behaving like some character in Gothic Novel, led us into one of the small bedrooms at the back of the house, pulled up a trapdoor in the wooden floor. Lawrence was immediately alert to this. *This was different. This was Some-thing.* We were all keen now to see "The Ingleza's *Bathroom*".

A crude wooden ladder went steeply downwards beside a rock wall. *Kyria* Rhoda babbled incessantly at Pippa, the only one who could understand her properly. We arrived in a vast underground cavern, the Cellar/storeroom in the old days – where the barrels for wine and olive oil, and all paraphanelia were kept, even the sheep and the goat.... It had its own entrance onto the lane at the front of the house.

We found ourselves looking at a modern bath sitting on a dirty rock floor, a lavatory and a washbasin plumbed into the un-mortared walls. A partition of old packing cases screened the area from the vastness of the rest of the cellar. It was Gorky's "Lower Depths".

Pippa said nothing. Ganga said nothing. I said nothing.

"I don't think I could take a bath down here," Ganga, murmured, " or even have a pee........" The mountain side would be preferable.

Lawrence's reaction was quite different. "Oh MUMMEE! This is SUPER!" enchanted by the idea of the trapdoor and the ladder into this underworld.

"We WILL keep this, won't we, Mummy?" How did he know this was the house she had decided on?

"I am not promising anything, Lol..."

"But, Mumm-ee....... its *SO nice*."

"We can't keep it like this, Lol..."

"We MUST keep the trapdoor in the floor. I want it! I'm going to live down here..... Can't I, Mumm-*ee*...." in his most importunate voice.

"I'm not promising anything, Lol..." but her mind was made up.

Ganga didn't say anything. I didn't say anything, knowing that nothing would deflect Pippa once her mind was made up.

She had found her place. ~~

2.
DUCK'S DEATH

"Duck's dead." Pippa said.

Not long after Lawrence had gone back to Athens, I knew Pippa was having difficulty with Duck, because Duck would insist on coming into the house, needing company.

"He makes such mess!" (No marble floors.) " I have to drive him out into the garden. The dogs hate him."

She doesn't get home till after dark each night.

"Duck is always the first to greet me. But last night when I came down the steps – no Duck. The dogs didn't rush to greet me either. They were being suspiciously furtive as if they knew. `Where's Duck?' I said. It was dark – I couldn't see anything. I got the torch, and there he was stretched out under the orange tree. He had teeth marks in his neck. The dogs didn't come near. `Which One of you Did IT? ' Pickle gave a whimper, and flung himself at me."

"I bet the duck went for his balls."

When Pickle was blissfully stretched out sleeping, his shiny brown testicles peeping out from his thick shaggy fur were irresistible to Duck – who would dive at them thinking they were edible.

"Yes, I think that's what happened. I dare not tell Lol..... I'll have to try and find another duck before he comes home..... By the way, "*Kyria* Rhoda has accepted my offer for the house," she says just before she disappears off to Athens to be with him because the latest couple looking after him are going away. "Now I've got to sell this one."

Before she leaves, she buys two ducks . "The man wouldn't sell me one. We can make a pen for them on the terrace..... "

But the new ducks are no substitute of DuckaDuck-Do-Dat. Witless silly things, scared of human touch. You can't have a relationship with them. They haven't been raised in an Athens Flat. They haven't his dignity – nor his regal character and personality. I just feed them. Nothing can replace Our Dear Darling Duck. We still have the rabbit. I don't take to the Budgerigar someone has dumped on her.

When Pip rings up from Athens to say, "I've got a buyer for the house." I feel the roof has been taken off my head.

"He's from another island, but is opening a restaurant on the road near you, and needs a house nearby. He's giving me a good price – enough to cover the cost of the new house , and reparations I think...." quoting what seems an astronomical figure in drachmes. "We bought the original cottages for £400 20 year ago so it's a pretty good deal.... His name is Solon. So if he should turn up wanting to look around – That's who he is... I'll be back soon anyway. I've got so much to do.... I've found a couple from South Africa with a child of their own, who will stay in the flat and look after Lol."

I was nursing the rabbit on the sofa one wet afternoon when I was startled by a knock on the door. It was raining cats and dogs. The rabbit leapt off my chest and dived into the bottom of the settle where Nellie was soundly sleeping. A neighbour would identify themselves by calling out. I opening the door apprehensively to a man standing on the doorstep. It was the new owner. He was a bit puzzled at the furtive way I begged him to come in, talking about a free range rabbit..... until the Rabbit suddenly popped out from the bottom of the settle, and bounded round the room.

Rabbit popping out of settle

He smiled. He spoke excellent English. As he stepped inside folding his umbrella, his eyes went immediately to the ceiling. I understood why he had come to see his new property, on the wettest afternoon for weeks.

"Does the roof leak at all?" he gently asked.

"Oh, no...." a white lie..... or a wet one. There were occasions when buckets had to be employed, in the kitchen.

He looked relieved – "May I see the other rooms?"

He went through the place, giving the walls a once over again, before saying, "Thank you very much. You can tell Mrs. Pippa she can collect the next installment of the money whenever she likes...." Putting up his black umbrella he left, still casting glances left and right at the garden.

Pippa rang up in the evening as if she had sensed his visit.

"He asked if the roof leaked.... It wasn't leaking, so I said No."

"Oh, good," sounding relieved.

"And the mice were off duty in the larder , thank goodness, when he looked in there. He can find out about them for himself...."

"Oh good." she said. "I've got so much to do about the new house. I'll be back next week."

I put Rabbit in her cage, bid her goodnight. Shut up the dogs. They sigh deeply and take to their beds, knowing I will be back first thing in the morning. It is hell feeling my way down the uneven steps in the dark. I feel sad – our life is changing – soon they won't be 'just up the Olive Grove'. There isn't an Olive Grove anymore.

3.

THE NEW HOUSE

When Pip comes back we chase off to the new house. The way up to the village if full of almond trees in blossom, standing like a procession of bridesmaids all the way down into the valley below the village and wild flowers everywhere.

I get the shock as we stand in the door way of the house, looking into a void. Everything has been ripped out from roof to basement .

"They had to make a new roof – so that made it possible to have skylights in the kitchen. Don't you see – now we can do what we like with it," she says. "We've got to think how to make the rooms, where to put the staircase, where to put the bathroom," undaunted by it.

This is her form of creativity. I haven't got the guts to gut a house and build it up again. I would just live in it as it was and make do.

The 'Masterbuilder' is walking like a ballet dancer along an exposed beam with a 10 ft drop into the cellar.

"We are lucky in him. He is excellent. He will do whatever we tell him – and he's got good ideas of his own. He says he enjoys working on an old house like this. He did his apprenticeship with an old village craftsman-builder. He finds making cement houses boring but good money, of course. My idea" she continues, "is to make the two back bedrooms into one big room. with the bathroom where the corridor was. And in this Saloni – we can have the staircase curving round a bit and going up from that corner opposite the front door. And instead of that ridiculous landing with the silly little bedroom , we can make a bathroom and two small bedrooms upstairs. I am determined to have a walk in wardrobe in my bedroom. I have always wanted one. It will have to be right under the roof, but never mind if I have to crouch a bit."

"What will you do with the basement?"

"That will have to wait. The money won't run to that yet. But I want the door down into it from the corner over there. "

"And out the back we can make a little garden in the ruined bit, because that is mine too. In Summer we can eat out there. It will be shady and nice."

Returning to the car, she says, "Let's go for a walk up there," indicating the ridge above the village. We drive up the winding road with the 25 hairpin bends, and take a walk along the saddle of the mountain following old donkey paths between dry stone walls, supporting old vine terraces with breathtaking views across the sea to the mainland mountains. All we encounter are two sheep and their new born lambs and one old man guarding them, who accosts us with surprise. "Who are you? Where are you going?"

"Pou thená (Any where)" Pippa says gaily;

"But that way goes NOWHERE," he insists.

"That's where we want to go! " she tosses back at him over her shoulder as we go on.

This is the Nowhere we both discovered when we came to this island years ago. We recognised it instantly and knew we must have it, instead of the Modern World.

Here, on a Spring day like this you might have a sighting of the Great God Pan asleep under an ilex tree by a stone built Bothie. We discover one immediately with a stone table, an outside cooking place, a well for water and some gnarled dwarfish vines. The idea that there are still these deep timeless fissures in the mountain untouched by the main roads and the new ugly buildings. Cradled in the groin of the mountain is this patchwork of small holdings with vines, vegetables, fruit trees, and full of butterflies and wild orchids.

On the way back to the car we pass the old man again who plaintively asks, "What time is it?"

"He has lived with a time to get up, a time to eat, a time to take the sheep up the hill, a time to head back to the village, and time to sleep....and now he wants to know what time it is?"

"What time *is* it really?" I ask, wondering what the future will be.

"The *Best* Time – Now. "
"The Time to do what you are doing."
"Yes!" certain of it.

~~~~~~~~~~~~~~~~~~~~~~~~~

ATHENS Sunday
TO THE BEST PERSON IN THE WHOLE WIDE WORD

Dear Mummy,

I am so looking forward to coming home. Elfy, Evie and her father are out down at Piraeus or somewhere.

Every morning I have an egg and some toast and take a toast to school. I sometimes have some lunch and if Elfy is at home I get a cooked supper. I had a very nice lunch today quite a rarity that Elfy made, but Trayzer cooked better specially on Tuesdays and Fridays

Chris and Elsie's huge Ariston washing masheen and a TV have arrived. Juging from the size of the box the TV must be collosul and my little washing mashine was thrown onto the balcony but I brought it in and I think I will put it in its box for safe keeping.

I have too much homework. I have been going to school by bike instead of bus. It is cheaper until you get a puncher. I have got to go and have a bath and eat so see you after.

Hellow again I had a shower and 2 toasts. By the way those eggs you bought me how long will they last? I have eaten about 3 and have boiled them for 10 min. but they were never just right. How long should I boil them for?

The poor cat *[Kit-kat-Kettel now renamed Sam]* is having a very bad time. He cannot sit down without being kicked or swung around on the end of his tail by Evie. I notice he is getting more aggressive and likes to bite and scratch. Oh well.

My big toenail came off. Goodbye, Write soon. I miss you. I love you. Send my love to Trayzer

Love Lawrence X X X X X X X X X X X X X X X X X X x 100 /100
X X X X X X X x 6.02 x 10 /23

~~~~~~~~~~~~~~~~~~~~~~~~~

He still can't spell….

4.

I went up to the house; going over to switch on the radio, I saw through the kitchen window – Nellie lying inside the Ducks pen, looking like a seal who had been clubbed on the head but not quite stunned. I rush out to her, realising from the smell she has been poisoned. I must do something – I don't know when Pip will be back. I call the Vet. the one who came to my aid the last time.

"But I am ill myself," he says." I haven't been away of my bed for three days..."

"Oh, please don't bother.... I'll find somebody," though I don't know of any other Vet. The English Vet has gone.

"No, I will come for *you*." he gallantly insists. What would I do without this man?

Going back to Nellie, I take in the full extent of the situation: one duck stiff, the other standing up, wings stretched out, is in process of dying. I hold it on the table as the luckless thing starts its death throes with just the same fluttering movements as Pavlova's 'Dying Swan'.

This has to be a deliberate act of poisoning. Whoever it was had to come right into the garden. Ducks are greedy things who gobble up anything and Nellie is a greedy girl too – if she saw the Ducks getting something – she would go for it. Or was it the other way round, something was given to Nellie, and when she sucked it up the Ducks rushed in. Ducks will eat anything.

The Vet. arrived looking as white as a sheet and quite groggy. He gave Nellie three injections, then had to take a tablet himself. He instructed me how to give her spoonfuls of magnesia every 15 minutes. He was loud in condemnation of the way the Greeks poison animals, saying "I am not Greek! I am `Venetian' and my mother was from Cardiff!" He goes.

I have to drag poor Nell out of the Ducks pen and get her onto one of the dog mattresses. She could just walk with me holding her under the belly. Poor Nellie Jelly-belly! The flies were getting onto her because of the filth she had been lying in. I clean her up.

Then I had to bury the ducks. I laid their stiff bodies in the trench Lawrence had dug in a moment of boredom, but had to bring loose earth from the building site in the Olive grove to fill the hole.By the time Pip walked in, I had enough of this day.

"What's happened ?" On hearing the story, "That settles it – I'm going to take that woman to court. Cassy was poisoned in Dominic's garden. Somebody threw poisoned meat over the fence, and the chap who has the taverna – his dog has died too."

After four days and nights of intensive care – from me by day and Pippa by night, Nellie has resurrected. Lovely to see her wagging her tail. Yesterday she was able to go out to do her business and come back in. She loves being fussed over, and having the constant little meals we had to give her. She will be surprised when it suddenly goes back to only one meal a day.

Pippa goes back to Athens to look for someone to live in the flat, but she is due back here are the start of the season. If she can't find new people to take over the flat – it will be my turn again.

5.

PUNKY-DOODLE-DOO

This morning coming up to the house I find two back packs in the dog room. Who knows where I leave the key? The next thing I see is a strange figure coming down the path dressed in a black mandarin cotton jacket and trousers, head shaved except for a tuft of hair heavily dyed black flopping over one eye, followed by a girl in jeans and jacket, with short blonde hair who looks like a boy. Who are these people? Are they people?

"Hullo, Trayzer! Hope you don't mind – we left our stuff inside. I remembered where you keep the key...."

Steve with shaven head

"Steven?!" the nice chubby boy from Wales who spent a summer with us how long ago now?

"Well – this is amazing!" not finding it easy to look at the safety pin piercing his nostril, and connected by a chain of safety pins, to his ear lobe. His trousers have holes burned in them, and bits of black tape strung web fashion between both legs.

"Isn't it difficult to walk like that?" I can't help asking,

"Oh, you get used to it." unabashed. This is not the Steven we knew, who was shy and sensitive. "I've just been round to Athena to ask about Pippa and Lawrence. She didn't seem to know me." *I am not surprised. She was probably considerably frightened.*

"Pippa and Lol are in Athens...."

"Oh. Fab! We're on our way there – hitching to Istanbul.... Perhaps we could see them...."

Pippa phoned in the evening; she hasn't found anybody. "Can you take the Bus on Friday? I tried to ring you before. Then I rang Athená. She said somebody has turned up.. and sounded quite worried. Who is it?"

"Steven."

"Why didn't Athena recognise him?"

"There's a reason for that..." cautiously. "They are hitching to Istanbul via Athens......"

"Why don't they come with you... they can stay here ... we'd love to see them."

Steve and Alice immediately decide to forego hitching to Athens to come with me on the bus.

I have to organize myself for Athens, see to Steven and Alice`s sleeping arrangements, cook for them, talk and listen. A dog has followed them from the harbour. It will not go away. At this point we do not need more animals. I pour water on him, throw stones – he goes and comes back. They'll be nobody here tomorrow, so that will be that.

At supper, with plenty of Retsina, I learn much. They are both studying German and Russian at Heidelburg University. He calls himself a `Celibate Punk' and she calls herself `a frustrated Lesbian'. This makes an excellent travelling partnership. He explains the safety pins in his nose and ears send the message `Safe Sex'. What it is to be young these days...

As I leave them for the night, "Get yourselves down to the bus station tomorrow by 6 a.m. Okay? Leave the key where you found it. Athena will come to feed the animals....."

Negotiating the neck-breaking stairway in the dark, I realise I forgot to say farewell to the house. I won't be going there again. When I get back from Athens , Pippa will be at the new house. This one won't be her home anymore. Its been my home too – these 10-11 years... Lawrence growing up from 3 to 14. Its the end of a chapter....I am almost afraid to turn the page.....but Pippa isn't. ~~

It was an embarrassing journey. Steven's appearance causes smirks and laughter, and ejaculations of "Aids!!"

"I expected some sort of reaction in Greece." he says unperturbed, "I thought to modify my appearance a little – I usually have my hair standing on end in six inch high spikes, dyed magenta." but for the Mediterranean he had modified it by shaving his head just leaving the one lock of jet black hair. "They throw beer bottles at me in Heidelberg...."

It suddenly dawns on me, as we enter the bus, that the passengers presume these are my children! What else are they going to think. I am glad I am wearing a skirt and that my coat is thoroughly bourgeois. It makes no difference. Will Lol go this way, too? No, he is going be a trained SAS cold-blooded killer. How difficult it must be to be a parent these days..... glad I avoided it.

On arrival at the flat, Pippa and Lawrence are speechless at Steven's transformation.

"No wonder Athena didn't know you...."

We have a lively supper in the kitchen, talking animatedly about several forms of sex. Lawrence silently taking it in, as we discuss lesbianism, homosexuality, drink too much and finally falling into our beds, and go out like lights.

Next day, Pippa leaves, taking the fully grown 'Kit-cat-Kettle', renamed 'Damn Sam', with her. Steve and Alice stay on for a few days to see the Acropolis and other things and come back with incredible stories. Eating their picnic on a park bench, a man had gone into the nearby bushes and dropped his pants for their benefit. Some Greek Punks seeing them from a bus, leapt off and ran back to greet them, inviting them to a Punk party, but Steve and Alice are leaving tomorrow. "Pity really – it would have been great."

I didn't know we had any Punks – inconceivable in the Greece I came to. Greece must be catching up.

I show them where to take the bus to the big National highway out of Athens north to Thessalonica, where they intend to sit by the road until they get a lift. I wish them luck. Young people have a lot of courage. Hopefully they will end up back in Heidelberg.....

6.

HOLLOW-GHOOLY-LAND AGAIN

So here I am back in `Hollow Ghouli-land'. This morning the buzzer went on the door. It was the Postman indicating I had to sign for a package. I drag on a shirt and shirt, take the lift. One of the vigilante women was with the postman. She left without a word, making it obvious that I am not the sort of person they want in this block of flats, but the postman is intrigued by my foreignness. We have one of those ridiculously intimate conversations I often find myself having with Greek taxi drivers.

"You English?"

"Yes."

"This your husband?" pointing to Lawrence's Greek surname on the envelope. It is from Pippa sending us the money she couldn't give us before she left. "No" I say.

"You not married?"

"No."

"You live alone?"

"No."

"Who you live with?"

"Mia fili moo…(A friend)" giving the female gender.

"Oh," he says. Now he is thinking I'm a lesbian.

Who should come through the hall as the postman is asking me if I live alone, but the `Hollow Ghoulissa' herself, like a galleon in full sail. She acknowledges the postman, ignores me, apart from looking down at my bare feet. I was in too much of hurry to find my shoes.....

Yes. I am back in `Hollow-*Ghouli*-land'.

In the evening Lawrence reduces me to pulp insisting I try the IQ test for Japanese children aged nine they had been given at School that day.

"This is a bus, Trayzer...." showing me an oblong box-like drawing with two windows in the side and two wheels under it. "Which way is it going?"

"I wouldn't want to travel on a bus like that....." playing for time.

"Come on, Trayzer – *try* . It is absolutely logical if you think about it," he says with confidence, knowing the answer.

I stare at the beastly mark.

"Think, Trayzer...which side of the road do you drive on?" giving me the clue – if I could use it.

"I have never wanted to emulate a Japanese child of nine....."

The answer when it comes, absolutely floors me.

"There is no door, only windows," he points out. "*Therefore* it is travelling to the left – in Greece, and the right if it were England. I'll give you another one, Trayzer."

"I don't WANT anymore!" thoroughly humiliated.

"Just try this one – *you might get it*."

"Are you insulting me or encouraging me?"

The next diagram posed the question "Which way is this car travelling?" the answer hinging on the driver's mirror! I am totally demoralized.

"Okay! Okay! I am obviously unfit for this Brave New World."

"Why do you get so angry, Trayzer? It doesn't *mean* anything." So he isn't taken in by this kind of thinking. "*Easy does it Old Girl...*"

"Why do you say that?"

"That's what you say coming down the mountain. "*Easy does it, Old Girl* – you say...."

"That's because I'm frightened of falling. Most people think it is God talking to them. I know it is Me."

"I never talk to myself," he says.

"You *do*! Ganga told me you used to talk to Seven little ladies when you were 4 -5 years old. Wherever you went the seven little ladies went too. You insisted on helping them over gates. She said it was a damn nuisance waiting for the Seven Little Ladies to catch up... you wouldn't go on without them."

"I don't remember.." typical male reaction , forgetting the seven little ladies he knew before he was five.

Saturday, we go to buy him a saw, nails, screws and paint, his very best things. Immediately we got home – (this is *not* "home" – it is only a Flat – what could be more flat than a flat) he starts making a little work table for himself. He had only been banging for about 10 minutes when the old lady ,who's balcony joins ours, stuck her head round the partition screaming that we are disturbing the whole block of flats.

He persisted until he finished the table, but it was the end of our creativity for the day. One can't do anything natural in an artificial environment.

The next weekend, I said without thinking, "You said you were going to fix the hinge on the kitchen cupboard."

"Well, if I can have 5 bangs of the hammer, I could."

"Oh, no, not five bangs..." remembering the Old Biddy next door.

"Just one then?"

"No, not even that! Do you want the old woman screeching over the balcony again? What a life we lead!"

"We don't *lead* it," he says, "*It* leads us. We trail along behind it."

He astonishes me with his perceptions. It is true, one is only half alive under these circumstances.

From the balcony gazing up at the mountain, I say "We've got to get back up there, Lol. "

"Can we go tomorrow. It's Sunday."

"Yes! Let's."

We set about preparing the sandwiches and the ovaltine.

7.

UP THE AIRY MOUNTAIN...

We started at 4 a.m. though Lol wanted us to start at 3. We were a bit querulous with each other on the ascent. I insisted we go one way; he didn't insist sufficiently that it was the other way, he had his stomach cramps, so I got my way and was wrong, but we saw a toad in the light of the torch.

It was hard work; the light in the sky was getting stronger so quickly we missed the stars. "If we had got up at 3...." he said.

The higher we got it was more toilsome. I haven't done this sort of thing for a while.... where the hell was the little Pine tree that means we have reached the saddle where it flattens out a bit? We got onto it just as the sun appeared. Immediately we became more cheerful and talkative. From here it is easy going to reach our Bivouac. But was not very warm; our hot ovaltine was the Nectar of the Gods. He was happy to stay within the Bivouac to continue his rebuilding work on the walls.

Once the sun was up it got hot. I had to seek some shade and found it quite near under the pine trees. More butterflies this time: A Brimstone, a Painted Lady, some small Coppers and Blues, Walls and Browns; a huge dragonfly of brilliant blue flew over and back with the searching importance of an army helicopter. Rock roses, sages, thymes all over the place.

I called Lol. "Come see how nice it is here." He came, and wandered deeper into the shady pines finding an even better place with a deep bed of pine needles to lie on and an almost unspoiled view over the landscape to the South, away from Athens. It was So Quiet – no other two footed thing came by; sunlight illuminated the arbutus in patches of bright green.

He tries to kill horseflies. As usual he says, "We could sleep up here.....Trayzer....."

He found the skeleton of a little bird folded as it would have been inside the egg – a thing of wonder, like a prehistoric burial artifact.

"Look, it has traces of feathers. I shall keep it forever," he says.

Descending the mountain, he suddenly looks back at me on the path above him,

"You look....umm…" trying to find the right words, "made up of..... different things..."

"What do you mean?"

"Like ..umm…..a Consequences picture…"

"What's that?" too old to know these things.

"You've got sports shoes like a kid – track suit trousers – *they're* alright …. but your jacket is dangling things.... and then you've got a straw hat like ...." searching for it.. "a Mexican...."

"I need the hat for the sun!" I protest, "and the magnifying glass on a cord, to look at wild flowers and insects," irritably realising he would not like to have to introduce me to his friends. As we set out in the dark nobody sees me, but when we come down from the mountain in the afternoon we must pass the café's with people sitting in them.

"What a sight we must look," he says uneasily.

"You mean *me!* You don't have to walk with me. You can walk on the other side of the road if you want...."

"It doesn't *matter*, Trayzer," he says gallantly and stays with me, like a real gentleman. ~

8.

My first Sunday, two failures turn out to be successes. I put the eggs on to boil, forgot them, panicked and they turned out perfectly. "This is the best egg I've ever had," he said.

Then he started to make a bread and butter pudding. We muddled through that, me going by the book, he saying "Mummy doesn't do it like that. She doesn't use eggs."

"The recipe says 2 eggs..." We put in two eggs. The oven is always guesswork. What came out was a surprise to us both. A bread pudding soufflé, delicious and as light as air.

"Now, " I said, "the third success would be to find a baby tortoise on the mountain."

We miss `Staunch Mabel' who had been released into the wild behind the new house in the village. After a long thoughtful pause she had waddled off – never to be seen again. We painted a mark on her shell so we might recognise her if we should meet her again. We feel lost without an animal. Pippa took 'Damn Sam' back home with her.

We took a walk on the nearest bit of the rough ground where they are creating the stadium. Lots of wild flowers out- Nature doing Her stuff; and we saw the goats – a magnificent Billy goat, two or three females and six baby goats jumping about butting each other.

"What a sight for the middle of a capital city! Pity we can't keep a goat on the balcony...."

Suddenly, there at my feet was a baby tortoise. We carry it home in triumph.

"We must give this one a special name."

"`Desirée'" I suggest, interpreting it as `Desire of the mountain.' "

But she ends up as 'Mabel II'. ~~

9.

PERCY

From our balcony I watch the Hollow Ghoulissa's husband fiddling importantly with his car – not the engine. He wouldn't know a thing about that. No, he opens the boot and the bonnet – to air it. He is portly and bespectacled, hair thin and stuck down on the scalp.

'We are the hollow men the stuffed men…' and they keep alive that arthritic deformed poodle, as if it has had to absorb all their poisons. What a trio. They don't look particularly Greek. You could put them down in Swiss Cottage, or Bournemouth and not know they were foreign to the place because they are not foreign to Suburbia. Suburbia is a country. They are quintessential suburban. It is quite obvious that we are the illegal immigrants in their world.

It gives me a thrill of excitement when the itinerant market assembles in our street. This morning I discovered a stall selling among the combat shirts and trousers, black wool Balaclavas and bought one for him and one for me – for our nights on the mountain.

He was thrilled with them, and made me put mine on, pulling the lower part right up to my eyes, and making me hold a knife between my teeth.

"You look like a real terrorist, Tray-zer!"

I point out that the Balaclava was probably invented by Florence Nightingale to keep the troops warm in the Crimean War. 'It was not invented for Terrorists!'

Coming home from school, he says, "There's a cat on the stairs, Tray-zer."

'So?' without responding

Next day :

"The cat's still there, Tray-zer. Come and see…"

Crouched against one of the faceless doors on landing below is a fully grown white cat with sandy ears.

"Perhaps he got in when the downstairs door was left open… people in these flats don't go in for pets except for the Hollow-Ghoulissa's arthritic poodle upstairs."

"No, Trayzer… I saw the people from that flat moving out the other day. They must have left him behind. Shall we..?"

"Better not – they might come back for him."

"But he must be hungry, Trayzer…."

"Well, bring him some milk." He went back upstairs to get some milk. The cat drank the milk said, 'Miaow – thank you.' but made no effort to ingratiate himself.

"He's a very sad cat, isn't he, Trayzer…"

Percy the cat

He looked for the cat every day, and took him food, then just appeared carrying the cat. "Nobody has come back for him. Shall we call him Percy?"

So we acquire Percy, a nice animal but the least entertaining of all the animals we have adopted. He never cheered up in his new circumstances, never got over the trauma of being abandoned by the people who had nurtured him initially. He remained in permanent state of depression. ~~

10.

WHAT IS INTELLIGENCE?

On Saturday afternoon we take our walk around the quarry with an eye to useful rubbish. He found an old washing machine which had nothing left on it save the programming switch. He was ecstatic. Out came the all purpose Swiss Army knife to undo the screws, and the saw blade to saw through the plastic knob – hard work, but he persists. Finally the screws, bolts and the multiple switch itself are put in my pockets. Then he breaks up a pile of expired street lamps to take the resisters off them, "Because you can't buy them, Trayzer," and ends by throwing up the great light bulbs which exploded with a delicious pop – all part of a Saturday afternoon's entertainment.

"Do you do this sort of thing with Pippa?"

"No – only with you , Trayzer."

In the evening he subjects me to another Japanese IQ test. This time it is the twins: one who tells the truth and one who tells lies. They are at a place where a road divides.

"You have to ask the way, Trayzer. What question do you ask to get the right answer?"

" I haven't a clue...." giving up at once.

"The answer is `What would your brother say?'"

"What does that prove?" mystified.

"*If* it is the one who lies, he will say the *wrong way*. And if it is the truthful brother ,he will say what his brother would say. *i.e. the un-truth.* So you *do the opposite* to what <u>either of them</u> has said."

"That's ridiculous! Why should he say what his brother would say – " now completely baffled. "It's nonsense!"

He comforts me by saying only 1 in 20 get it right.

"I should hope so! He must *the only stupid* one – *stupid* enough to *understand* such a STOOPID QUESTION! If *this* is what intelligence is based on we'll end up as Aliens on our own planet! But it isn't new, Lol. they used to be called Riddles – The Delphic Oricle, The riddle of the Sphinx – and Oedipus. They were Greek then – now they are called "Intelligence tests" and are Japanese!"

"What's Edipuss?' thinking of a cat.

"You mean to say – here you are in Greece, and they don't teach you about Oedipus or the Riddle of the Sphinx? Well, that goes to show..."

At supper in the kitchen he suddenly gets up to demonstrate an SAS technique, putting a strangle hold on my neck and his hand over my mouth. I couldn't throw him off and panicked. It was like being held under water. When he releases his grip, I am really shaken. "You MUST NOT DO THAT!"

"Why?"

"You nearly killed me, Lol!"

"I was only joking...."

"*Some* joke. You don't know your own strength." flinging out of the kitchen to recover in my bedroom.

He comes to the door, less sure of himself. "I do it hundreds of times to my friends...."

"You shouldn't – its dangerous."

"*Please* forgive me, Trayzer... *I didn't mean it*. I won't ever do it again." He goes off to his room. We are both shaken – we are so dependent on each other in this artificial setting.

When I have recovered my cool I go to find him.

"It's alright , Lol, don't you want the bedtime story?"

He is sitting at his desk fixing my radio. I asked him if he could fix it days ago, and he didn't do it. Now he is doing it to please me and make things alright. He is always surprising me.

I have to fight for authenticity as an Adult – realising for the first time how fragile it is. I am learning to appreciate a child's understanding of grown up things before experiencing them as an adult. Children observe and absorb everything and know if it rings true or false. In my case – is it *The child is father to the woman?* We love and hate each other with a deep mystical way which cannot be falsified by either of us. We never touch, hug, or kiss.... our relationship is pure friendship. It has to be that – or it is nothing..... ~~

11.

NIGHT ON A BARE MOUNTAIN

At 9 pm. we set off to spend the night on the bare mountain in our dustbin bags. White clouds were approaching out of the North East, but the wind herded them away.

We didn't get as high as last time. He could have gone on, but I was fed up already opting for nearest Pine trees. He made a nest for himself under the tree. I chose a flat bit close by – under the stars – because I like looking up at the stars and wriggled into my Municipality Dustbin bag. This time he had taped my two bags into one shroud with a flap to pull over my head. We were both wearing our new woolly Balaclavas.

I hoped, having done it once., sleeping in a dustbin bag on mountain would be easier, – it wasn't; the length of a night doubles. The strong wind gusted continuously. I could not get warm; my bum was cold – I needed a Balaclava for my bum. We had no bedding to lie on – just the ground. Before leaving the flat I had caught up the loose ironing board cover, thinking "That might be useful....." Now I wrapped it round my loins and it made a significant difference. Curled up like a hedgehog, I must have slept a bit because when I looked up at the sky again, the Pleiades had moved and Orion was visible. I enjoy the stars – feeling them moving – but not fast enough tonight. I groped in my back pack for the chocolate coconut bar, a few units of heat. A beautiful experience nibbling at it like a rodent inside my Municipal Dustbin bag. Now I know the pleasures in the life of a rat.

He woke up, saying his knees were stiff.

"What about mine? they are 40 years older than yours."

We had some cocoa from the flask and I gave him the other chocolate coconut bar. I had brought two. The wind was really strong now. He had the nerve to say it wasn't windy.

"I don't see the branches moving," he said.

"You don't have to look at the branches to feel the wind."

At 5 am. he had the cramps and got up to walk around. Only one more hour to endure of this! As soon as it was light enough to see the way down, I packed up my things.

"I'm going!" I said, stomping off down the path, while he still stayed in his bag.

As my blood quickly warmed up and the sky lightened, everything became attractive again. Go back to the flat – to do what? I hate the flat. I turned back up the hillside. He was still in his bag, quite happy.

"Let's make some soup," I said with enthusiasm. This needed his expertise with the camping stove. He was slow to move. I got furious again. The more furious I become the less he co-operates. I insisted we find a place out of the wind to make a fire to boil our soup.

"We are doing this for *You*, you know," I savagely point out. "To test your survival techniques and all you can do is lie in your bag."

"But I *am* surviving, Trayzer," he points out, "by keeping warm."

"Well, I'm NOT!"

"That's because you don't have the right attitude, Trayzer..."

"To hell with the right attitude – I want some soup."

He moves slowly, and then sets about trying to light the fire by rubbing two sticks together.

"For God's sake, Lol! Use the lighter!" Persuasion and reasonableness is what Pippa uses. I must learn not to rage. It achieves the opposite to what I am raging about. But damn it – I want my soup. The packet soup was comforting and put me into a good mood again.

We didn't go on up to the Bivouac. The wind still strong and cool, would have been stronger and cooler at the top. And the joggers were chugging up the same path – this one route to the to the top becomes the M.1. on a Sunday. We both loathe having to greet people puffing up. On Saturdays we have the place to ourselves.

We found a place off the beaten track under the Pine trees where nobody comes by. We had plenty of sandwiches, cocoa, and more packet soup. He set about making another fireplace very skillfully. Watching him, I say, "Oh, Lol – I hope you don't end up in a collar and tie, behind a desk." It was heartfelt.

"Don't worry, Trayzer..." he replies confidently. "I won't." But he doesn't he know what life can do. Pippa wants him to go to University.

Suddenly we saw a weasel – slinking across the rocks – the only wild life – apart from the huge bats we had seen in the night above the Pine tree.

"We will come to this place again won't we, Trayzer."

"You bet. Rather a weasel than a panting jogger any day." utterly jubilant now. "Oh, what a letter I am going to write about this night's work...."

"Why, Trayzer... ?" puzzled.

"I only DO this sort of thing in order to write about it!"

"Really? That's amazing. I wouldn't think of talking about it."

Back at the flat, he sits on the floor twiddling a specially shaped piece of wood like a fat flat pencil, on top of another piece of wood.

"Look – Trayz! Did you see?" He swears that a spark occurred. I have to get down on the floor, to peer hopefully awaiting a spark.

"I can't see anything except how long I am going to have to wait for my cup of soup next time.."

"Watch this..." He puts some sugar between the two pieces and certainly a spark flew off.."Would Aborigines have had sugar?" I query. ~~

12.

QUEEN ALICE

Saturday evening again, we are just getting ready to move onto the mountain, when Pippa walks in.

"Mummeee!"

"I just hopped on the plane. I didn't have time to warn you."

"You have spared me a night on the Bare Mountain!" glad to be able to sit down at the kitchen table and open a bottle of Retsina. "Another ten minutes, the flat would have been empty, except for a cat and a tortoise."

"This is Percy, Mummy." She immediately takes Percy onto her lap,

"How's the house coming on?"

"You'll be surprised when you come back. The bathrooms are in – though there's no door on the downstairs one. I've bought a wood burning stove for the sitting room, and an iron cooking range for the kitchen. I couldn't resist it. It weighs a ton, and the floor has got to be reinforced. I don't know how we can get it into the kitchen. It is down in the Apothiki for the time being...... I don't know quite how we are going to manage that..."

"Oh, Mummy –" he suddenly says, "Won't we ever go back *home*?"

"That's not home anymore, Lol. It belongs to someone else now."

"But my tree house is there...."

Percy purrs as her fingers explore his fur. "This cat has got a little scab on its head like a new born baby...." Then she suddenly says, "There's something else I have to tell you."

Pause: "I've been offered the job of British Consul. They just threw it in my lap. I don't know what to do....That's why I'm here really. I've got to go to the Embassy on Monday to discuss it."

"You'll be great!' I exclaim, remember when Alice becomes Queen in 'Through the Looking Glass! "Here's to `Queen Alice`!" raising my glass of Retsina. "Fancy the girl of 19 back packing to Greece, ending up as her Britannic Majesty's Representative 20 years later!"

"I'm not sure ...... I will have to be..... "

"*Different*?"

"Yes....."reluctantly. "I'm not sure if I can....'

"Oh, you've a cool head and a sound mind. You can do it."~~

Queen Alice

"Well, this is grand!" said Alice. "I never expected I should be a Queen so soon…. So she got up and walked about – rather stiffly just at first, as if she was afraid that the crown might come off: but she comforted herself with the thought that there was nobody to see her, "and if I really am a Queen," she said as she sat down again, " I shall be able to manage it quite well in time.

13.

'POXY' PERCY

With only a few days to the end of term, he wants to go down to Monasteraki on Sunday morning to look for a special kind of bolt for his bike. We wander through the alleys of the bazaar, looking at the junk laid out. We bought ourselves Combat hats at a kiosk. His has to be in DPM or camouflage. I choose a plain green one.

He spends a long time looking in the window of a smart hunting and survival shop.

"Oh, *come* on, Lol..."

"Wait – I haven't seen *everything* yet..." scanning the window like laser beam.

To keep myself going, I buy a cup of Salepi from a vendor with a huge brass samovar mounted on a little push cart. A glutinous, sweet drink laced with cinnamon – quite agreeable, and hot enough to scald.

We get back to the flats by strap hanging on a crowded bus. For once I was prepared to take the lift, though I hardly ever do, but he insists I walk up the stairs `like this Trayzer,' taking the steps three at a time on his young strong long legs.

"I would rather climb the mountain any night, than go down into Athens by day.." I say, toiling up behind him. Even he admits that central Athens is a tiring place.

Immediately he starts to waterproof his cap with beeswax simply rubbing it in and ironing it. This proves very successful, I do mine too. He is so pleased with his hat, he wears it even indoors and eats his meals wearing it. "I'm going to wear it until I go green with it," he says.

Sitting on the balcony in the noonday sun, my combat hat shielding my eyes, he says I look like a 'Wombat'.

"You mean: `An old bat in a combat hat'?"

Percy likes to lie on my chest and snuggle right up to my chin; he sleeps at night with Lawrence. A few days after Pippa's visit, I discover a bald patch on his head, just where Pippa said he had a scab like a new born baby. Lawrence has strange spots on his face, and body. I discover the same red spots on my arms. *What can it be and what must I do about it?* 'Ringworm' insinuates itself into my mind though I don't know what it is. "I think we've caught something from the cat."

This is all I need.... thrown into a frenzy of washing all the bed linen.

"The cat must sleep in the kitchen from now on."

I put Percy in the picnic basket to take him to the Vet. In the middle of the `Weird Wood', the surrealist phenomenon of Pine trees in serried ranks under which nothing grows, the cat managed to push its way out of the basket – pausing in astonishment at where he finds himself – like being on a different planet. He warily examines the nearest tree, before allowing me to pick him up and put him back in the basket which I tie more securely.

The vet confirms it is a fungus infection so it *is* Ringworm. The cat is renamed ` Poxy' Percy.

"So we are taking Ringworm home with us."

"But it won't be really home, will it...." he says sadly..

The journey back turns into nightmare as Poxy Percy, never transported anywhere, except in a basket to the vet, yowls in terror all the way to the airport. On the plane, Lawrence has him in the basket on his lap. On take off poor Percy, berserk with fright, thrusts his paws out of the basket clawing at Lol's jumper. We have to turn it quickly round against the back of the seat and cover it with his jacket. After that, despairing of life, Poxy Percy gave no more trouble.

"Perhaps he's died of fright?"

"Well, we will have to wait until we get home to see...."

Arriving over the island, Lol points to the rain passing horizontally over the windows in silver threads. We seem to be coming down, and then rising up again. This happens twice. The Pilot explains he has made two attempts at landing but conditions are `unfavorable', that we have enough fuel to stay half an hour over the island, that he would make another attempt to land in a minute, if that fails we would have to return to Athens.

The idea of returning to Athens and having to go through the whole procedure again, is overwhelming. Lawrence is studying his Morse Code manual with great attention. I study it with him. It concentrates the mind, trying to spell my name in dots and dashes…. And spelling

`Help' .and finally, `Dear God – if you're there, please……. but this proved too complicated....

On the third attempt we bump down on the runway and everybody breaks into spontaneous clapping .

Pippa is not there to meet us – too busy with her new role as `Queen Alice'. But Roy is there to pick us up in his jeep and ferry us out to the new house.

We are amazed at the transformation of the house though none of the rooms have doors yet, it makes it a bit embarrassing to go to the Loo. Trying to cook supper , I can't find the knives and forks – searching for familiar objects in unfamiliar places.

She walks in at 9 o'clock. "Sorry, I couldn't be there to meet you. "

He greets her with "Mummy, *why* did you get rid of the trapdoor..... You *promised*..."

"I didn't promise, Lol. We couldn't possibly keep it like that." Firm and reasonable.

"It was *so* lovely…. I wanted to live *down there.*" ~~

The strong smell of dust, paints and adhesives wrecks me. I pass an abominable night sleeping on the couch in the back room, which she says is going to be *a dining room `for when I give a dinner party…'* It doesn't sound like Pippa at all. Is this part of the new role of "Queen Alice"?

I get up early to climb the hill behind the house to watch the dawn. After three days, I find the house rather oppressive, the only outlook is from her bedroom upstairs. This is her burrow she is contriving it out of her instinctive DNA, her secret self, like an animal or a bee but it has a long way to go before living in it will be pleasurable.

"I think I'll go home now......" I say one morning.

"Why, Trayzer? "

"It's making me cough and sneeze..... and I need to see what is happening to my place."~~

14.

THE ME-NESS OF ME

The rediscovery of my little pad is like Mole rediscovering the burrow he abandoned to go with Ratty. Oh, it looked so nice after 96 days in Hollow-ghouli-Land. Dirty, and shabby – and though I don't own it – only rent it, it is My Place. The mugs , bowls, spoons, pots and pans exist because of Me, and for Me alone; anybody else would relegate them to the dust bin.

I spend a whole week enjoying the `Me-ness of Me', attending my flowers pots, writing letters, listening to the radio. Oh, to have back the *Me-ness of Me*. This *Me-ness* is a thing-unto-itself. I don't give a damn what anybody thinks of it. *This I Am*.

But there aren't any animals to tend – or the boy.....there is only Me..... *they* are no longer at the top of the olive grove. Sunday morning I walk to the town to catch the bus out to the village and *them* .

Pippa looking out her window at the view, sees me come up the rough path to the front of the house.

"Good heavens! I never thought you were capable of getting yourself up here!" She often underestimates me, I feel.

Adjoining the house is the ruin of another dwelling covered in ivy. It can't have been lived in for 50 or more years.

"I wish that bit belonged to me....." she says, "I thought of making an offer for it. The woman who owns it came up the other day, offering to sell it to me. She wanted more than I paid for the house and renovating it. But I've been told I can have it taken down, if it becomes dangerous..... That's something to know.... I could make it into a garden."

Lol comes whizzing round the corner. "Hullo Trayzer! Come and see this!" and takes me round the house to show me his workshop in the cellar beneath the kitchen.

"*Ree*-ally Nice isn't it, Trayzer.!" He has all his tools hanging up on the wall, there is a workbench – all his saws, screwdrivers, clamps – everything neatly arranged. "That's great, Lol."

"And this is my air pistol."

"Oh, my brother taught me how to shoot one of those when I was a kid. We used to shoot at old lamp bulbs against the garden wall." instantly regretting this gratuitous information for the light that comes into his eyes. Luckily, there are no used lamp bulbs.

A nice upright iron stove stands on its four claw feet in the sitting room, with the pipe going through the wall and out into the front porch.

"That was the easiest to install." says Pippa coming down the stairs. We'll need it in the winter....the only way to heat the place."

Suddenly I realise something is missing – the dogs. "Where are Nellie and Sofi?"

When we came from Athens I didn't notice their absence in a place where I never expected to see them. Only Pickle is with us and Sam the cat, who doesn't accept Poxy Percy as a cat at all, and simply ignores him.

"Oh," Pippa says, "we lost Nellie just before we left. After her illness she used to get confused, and started going off in the wrong direction. I had to leave her alone rather a lot – and suddenly she wasn't there anymore. I looked for her all over the place – but she never appeared. I saw a dog exactly like her in town, and went up to it. I was convinced it was her, and called 'Nellie!' but it wasn't."

"And Sofi?"

"Sofi didn't want to come. She made that quite obvious. She was not going to come in the car."

Sofi never came in the car as the other dogs did – leaping into the back seat with alacrity. "So I had to leave her there. Athena will look after her.... It was Sofi's choice."

"She was never really was one of us, was she....Paul was the only one she cared for."

"I'm not sorry frankly, not having had her spayed."

"But we've still got Pickolo-gino!" says Lawrence, having created yet another name for the hairy little hound, picking him up in his strong arms.

We went swimming, off the rocks at Nissaki, came back, and shoved things around in the house. "There is still so much to do. I want to decide where to put the pictures." So we do that. While down in the Apothiki, we looked at the new kitchen range.

"Why don't you get it into the kitchen, Mummy?"

"It weighs over 170 Kilos, Lol. I've had to have the floor reinforced to take the weight – "

"But ...Mummee...."

She ignores his plea, because she doesn't know how she is going to get this piece of extravagance into it's place. To fall in love with a Kitchen range is one thing, to get it into her kitchen is another. This is something yet to be solved; she walks away from the problem back up into the house.

I cook supper while they clear up the little courtyard behind the house, to put a table and chairs so we can eat out there. We have supper under the pergola with grapes dangling over our heads. The sounds of a Brass Band tuning up, and a burst of music come from below the house.

"They must be giving a concert in the forecourt of the Church. Lets go and see."

At the bottom of the alley, we lean on the wall looking down into the courtyard beside the church, where a group of young boys and girls clutching gleaming brass instruments – the piccolo player looks about twelve – are groping courageously through the New World Symphony; the conductor waving his hands about with graceful vigour expressing a dedicated determination to bring his pupils through the difficult music as the wind plays havoc with the music sheets.. Villagers make up a proud inattentive audience with children and babies running around, or clamped on grandmotherly laps. This is a real community still.

I begin to see virtue in Pippa's new life….. ~~

15.

THE SPANISH MAIN

I sleep in the back room. Next morning when she is ready to go to town, Pippa says, "Do you want me to take you home?"

"I'll stay with Lol...there's lots to do...." She goes.

He and I are drawn back to the new kitchen range by an unexpressed consensus. We stare at it.

"It's so nice, isn't it, Trayzer."

"Yes – it makes me think of a Spanish Galleon ...." So it acquired the name 'The Spanish Main'.

The Stove

He looks over it very carefully. "I think I can do something," he says. Running round to his workshop, he returns with a couple of screw drivers. He has spotted some screw heads on the enamel iron pilasters, and sets about unscrewing them. He gets them both off and then manages to remove the heavy doors to the oven, the fire box, and the ash box.

"That's brilliant, Lol! That's reduced the weight a lot. Perhaps we can do something with it now."

When Pippa comes home, he shows her what he has done. She isn't convinced, she is not usually this pessimistic, but rings up Roy. "He says he'll come and have a look at it tomorrow." which means I stay another night.

Next afternoon Roy turns up in jeep with his wife and team mate, Effie. He looks at 'The Spanish Main' thoughtfully – "Okay, we'll give it a try...."

He drives the jeep up the narrow lane to the door of the Apothiki, takes a wooden sledge contraption out of it and lashes it behind the jeep.

"If we can get it onto that – I can drive it up to the beginning of the alley."

Mr. Foti , the old man who lives in the front of the building, comes out to see what the ` foreigners' are doing, watching as we struggle to manhandle the heavy brute on to a wooden sledge. Roy drives it the short distance to bottom of the alleyway leading to the kitchen porch. Fine, but that is as far as it goes. Then we have to pull ,push, drag it on the wooden sledge to the kitchen porch. There are only the four of us; one man, two women and a small boy. *I begin to think I should have gone home.....*

Having got it as far as corner of the house, we sit around to take a rest, contemplating how to get it up the narrow steps of the Kitchen porch. It is hot. Effie takes off her T-shirt, revealing a chic black camisole top. `That's better,' she says. She is a slim elegant creature.

"It's a tricky one..." says Roy, observing the six deep steps to the covered porch , " no room to manoeuvre. "

Not only are the steps steep, there is a bulge in the wall. "Well, there's no going back." says Roy, and goes off to get a rope from the jeep.

The back Porch

"Pippa went off to work this morning with the intention of having nothing to do with this project. How right she was! I wish I'd gone too!"

Lawrence looks at me

"Well, there's nothing for it – everybody up!" says Roy, getting the rope firmly around the body of the Brute.

With Roy and Lawrence at the top of the stairs pulling and Effie and me pushing from below – the Brute begins to move at an increasingly steep angle. If it slipped back, Effie and I were in the position to be crushed by it.

"Oh, this is madness!' I protest. "It isn't worth wrecking ourselves for!" wanting to walk away from the whole thing. Lawrence looks silently down at me.

Slowly and painfully, the Brute arrives at the top of the narrow steps, then has to be tilted on end to pass through the kitchen door. Roy brought greased planks on which to slide it across the floor to the furthest side of the kitchen where it must go.

Suddenly – there it was – in position! Lawrence screws the pilasters back on and the doors. We sit around the kitchen table celebrating with tea and stronger liquor for Roy whose fuel is whisky.

Pippa came home that evening anticipating our failure. Entering by the kitchen, taking in the sight of the beautiful Spanish Main installed in the right place , and the smug look on our faces. she gasped. "OH! I *never* thought you'd do it...."

When Roy and Effie had gone and Pippa was upstairs having a shower, Lawrence, leaning against the kitchen wall, arms folded across his chest, confronted me. "*Tray-zer*..... Why were you so ready to give up ?"

"I was afraid. I was afraid we couldn't succeed and we could have damaged ourselves badly....."

"But, Trayzer ... it was *your idea* in the first place....."

"I was wishing I hadn't had it....Pippa didn't think we'd be able to do it, and she doesn't give up lightly. What if it had slipped down on Effie and me?"

"But .you tried to persuade *the others* to give up....." That was my crime.

"The problem is, Lol ... I *have too much imagination* and I am not very brave..... it's a bad combination..... I wish I were different, but I am not."

Without excusing me, he left it there. My cowardice was not referred to again.~~

16.

THE BRITISH EXPERIENCE

Tuesday is spent meeting Ganga, due to arrive at noon. Pippa is working, so Lawrence and I go to the Airport only to discover `All flights delayed.' We walk back into town which is full of pinkly perspiring 'TOORISTS' in their `little tops' and shorts, sun frocks, eating ice-creams, pizzas, and swigging ouzos and beers, and take the bus back to the village; an old fashioned `Dung beetle type bus with a ladder up to the roof for the baggage. The door opened by a handle, which has to be slammed hard to shut. It has been refurbished , smartly painted, and very clean. The driver is a piratical man with the close cut black beard of a Conquistador. High Tech had been installed above his head in the form of a radio and tape recorder with a microphone.

At 9 p.m. Ganga rings from the Airport to say she has arrived and will take a taxi. She staggers into the house at 9.30 p.m, after the 3 hour journey had been translated into 13 hours. So much for air travel. Slim, neat, elegant and resilient as ever, the only thing she wants to do is lie out flat on the kitchen floor. We offer her a bed or the settee.

"This is perfect... I'll be all right in a minute..." and she was. Typical Ganga.

She is surprised how the house has been transformed, though it is temporarily in even deeper chaos, a floor is being varnished, not to be walked on till Wednesday. So we have go out of the kitchen door round the house , cross by a bridge contrived by Lawrence to the front porch , enter the sitting room by the front door to get to the bedrooms.

Lawrence gets busy rigging up an electric light in the courtyard at the back of the house – though candles would be nicer. We set the table there, cook the meal, and wait for Pippa to come home. Children from the village creep like rabbits up the alley to peer at us. If we notice them, they run away giggling. Finally Pippa comes, apologizing, "Sorry, I'm late – we had problems...."

The evening is complete.

We spend the days swimming off the rocks. Lawrence snorkelling. From time to time, Ganga sits up alert as an animal, "Where is he? Oh, there he is...." and lies back again.

"What's it like being the mother of the British Consul, then?"

"It's put my stock up at home.... It is my trump card at parties. She seems to have taken to it like a duck to water."

"It was very amusing when the British community here heard that she was to be the new Consul. `Pippa who?' `Who's Pippa?' `Why wasn't it given to so-and-so? They would have been Much Better...' Now, they sing to another tune: *Pippa will know... ask Pippa.... Pippa will do it... Pippa is the best person to help ....* She 's invited to parties by the people who said `Pippa Who?' `Who's Pippa!' She takes it as it comes, but is not taken in by any of it. When you think of it, she was never `establishment minded', was she?"

"My children are full of surprises.... She says we have to go to a Cocktail party on board the British Ship in the harbour tonight. Are you coming?"

"Hardly my scene...."

"Oh come on. You are invited."

"Well, as you will be there, I might. It would be fun to see her in action though I haven't anything proper to wear....let's have another swim I'll think about it."

The party on board the British Naval ship was a weird experience. Climbing the gangplank to be greeted courteously by the Receiving Officer, I nearly trip getting off the gangplank on to the deck. Almost everybody tripped on boarding; two ratings, looking about 12 years old, stationed on either side of the gangplank were ready to catch them.

Pippa, smartly dressed, (she of the jeans and T-shirts) is cool, calm and collected. Ganga having been in the W.A.A.F's as a girl can take it all in her stride, too. Lawrence darts around looking at all the mechanical things. Only I am uneasy. Watching `Bistowe kid Brits' smelling the gravy of Olde England coming aboard. Waiters circulate with gin and tonics, wine and fruit juice and canapés. Everybody is chattering away, when the trumpeter boy – looking about as old as Lawrence, climbs up onto the bow. The Captain calls for silence. The boy raises his brass trumpet to blow the ritual sunset ceremony as the flag is lowered. It is like being at Boarding School again. When we are free to speak again, there is an audible murmur of appreciative emotion from the `Bistowe Kid Brits'. Even they don't choose to *live* in England anymore either.

It is a relief to escape down the gangplank and go home.

"Never again!" I say, "How does Pippa do it! After all, she didn't come out here to be one of them. She was running away from them ,too!"

"She says, it is just a job."

The fortnight with Ganga passes all too quickly. Seeing her off at the airport is another 'British' experience, though very different, among the over weight beer swigging tourists, dressed as for a Mardi Gras – with T-shirts reading PISSED AGAIN. LEGLESS .....NO PROBLEM. If this island is no longer the one I came to, neither is the island I left.~~

17.

BACK TO HOLLOW-GHOULI-LAND

The Summer holiday over, "Get yourself together, Lol. You're leaving tomorrow..." Pip urges him.

He takes no notice. He is in the bathroom, (which still has no door) bathing Pickle. Finally, I act as his amanuensis. "What do you need to take? Hammer.... screwdrivers?" knowing he can't be without his tools. "Yeah.... don't forget the vice..." I get them from his workroom under the kitchen and put them into the hold-all.

"By the way," Pippa suddenly says, "I've got a ticket for you.... It will only be for week or two. A couple are coming from Rhodesia to take over the flat and look after him.... they have children as well."

I've drawn the short straw again.. *Only she can do this to me.....*

Lawrence and Pickle emerge from the bathroom smelling of a hairdresser's salon.

"What did you use, Lol?" she questions him suspiciously.

"The stuff on the shelf."

She goes into the bathroom and comes out holding a near empty bottle. "Did you use this?"

"Yes."

"But , Lol! That's my *Best* Shampoo. It's *very* expensive."

"But he smells nice, doesn't he?" uncontrite.

Only he can do this to her......

We left in the dark of early day with the usual mountain of awkward luggage: bicycle, guitar, typewriter, tool bag, suitcases, and a kitten. `Damn Sam' and 'PoxyPercy' are staying, but we have a little ginger kitten that came to the kitchen door. We call him Tolstoy.

I contrived a harness to fit him with a lead, so we could let him out of the basket .He soon settled down quietly on the heap of baggage taking an interest in the unusual surroundings as if he had reached another planet. Lawrence had him on his shoulder at times. I had him on my lap in the plane. When we took off he was very anxious, and but didn't panic, then suddenly went into a cataleptic trance, his body becoming rigid between my hands. It was the same as we came down.

We spend 20 minutes waiting for our luggage to come up, half an hour in the taxi queue, half an hour in the taxi – at the sight of our luggage "You need a lorry for this lot!" the driver said, but didn't refuse to take us. I hate these journeys.....

We got everything into the lift without meeting the Hollow-Ghoulissa and any of the other vigilantes.

On opening the door of the flat, unlived in for three months ...... every surface seemed to move.... Then we see what moves: Cockroaches! Hundreds of cockroaches scampering in every direction at our intrusion.

We have been up since 5.30, have spent five hours taking a 45 minute flight. *This is all I need....*

Cockroaches... cockroaches... cockroaches... in everything : the cupboards under the sink, the insulation around the oven, in the gas stove, in the open packets of rice, sugar and coffee even in the fridge. Having had the place to themselves for the 3 months of the summer, they have had had a population explosion. The kitten ate three for breakfast.

At the Supermarket a wall of shelves is devoted to different brands of spray for cockroaches and Ants, "We're not the only ones, Lol. There must be a plague of cockroaches of Biblical proportions in this 'superior' suburb."

The flat is thick with 3 months dust.,not helped by the spray.

"Is it ozone friendly, Trayzer?"

"I bought the one that says so – "

"Do you think it's true...." He is a practical kid.

"I can't see how it can be. I only hope *we* survive it, never mind the ozone layer. "

We tie scarves around our faces and spend the whole weekend washing, cleaning, killing and spraying.

The cockroaches are the pinky bronze sort, not the black ones. They have a sort of innocence about them as they scurry away. I develop a rapid reaction of slamming my right foot down on them hearing them crunch. What passion it arouses. The adrenaline flows, as with slipper in hand as well as my rapid right foot action, I slam and bang. Lawrence rises to the challenge of cleaning and spraying, but is reluctant to kill them directly.

Sweeping and washing, cleaning, my legs and back ache... I feel years older.

"This is not my idea of fun! I'm supposed to be an Artist!" thinking of the tapestry I should be working on. "What *is* Woman's Lib?" I demand.

"Woman's what?"

"Nothing... I'm talking to myself..."

"*You* always do that. I *never* talk to myself," he says.

"I have the *best* conversations with myself – so don't interrupt."

And continue the debate in my head:

There is no such thing as Woman's Lib. A woman is never liberated from domestic obligations. There may have been a sexual liberation, but not a domestic one. Take Pippa, and women like her, who divorce and are determined to bring up their child on their own. A woman cannot bring up her child alone. As Ganga, says, it is much harder to bring up one child than three. It needs a whole team of people to be with one child. Woman is enslaved by her emotions anyway. I was emotionally free until I became involved with Pippa and Lawrence, now here I am, enslaved by a small boy, when I should be working a tapestry the size of a wall. I am trying to be an Artist.

It is not just the chores. You cannot be with a child of any age without finding yourself up to your neck in Socratic debate. The Why? Why? Why? It isn't enough to shop, cook, mop and sweep and not complain, and not be a martyr... you have to explain the unexplainable as well!

"Trayzer, here's some more..."

"Kill them!"

"I haven't got my shoes on...."

17.

TOLSTOY

Hearing us working in the kitchen, the old woman next door starts rattling the bottles she keeps on her side of the partition – she kept it up for about 20 minutes.

"Why is she making all that row?"

Remembering the trouble with the tortoise I had made sure the gap is filled so the kitten can't get through. I can't bear the noise she makes, it's an invasion of privacy..

"Probably wants attention. She's been alone for three months. Ignore her...."

We go back to our work dismantling the old stove to get at the gunge of ages. More cockroaches emerge out of the insulation.

Suddenly the old woman is screaming "I know you're there!" and the next minute there is a ringing of our door bell. I freeze like a rabbit. "I'm not going to answer it....." I'm in my old trousers and dirty T-shirt. "Where's Tolstoy?"

"He was watching the partition – where the old woman is."

Lol peers cautiously out of our kitchen door at the partition. "He's gone.... she's pulled out the wood.... he must have gone through."

"Then it's her fault!"

Next she is back at the partition shouting like an old witch.

"She says she'll tell the police we keep snakes...." Says Lawrence, hopping up and down with glee.

"Oh, my God! I can't stand this sort of thing..." distraught.

"Why do you let it bother you, Trayzer! I don't care."

But we are talking in whispers. The next thing we know, she has chucked Tolstoy back over the partition.

"Quick Lol – find something to bung in the gap...." grabbing up Tolstoy and shutting him in the bedroom. Later, I find he has done a wee in the middle of my bed, in protest at being barred from the action.

Kitten. Tolstoy

At supper we move the kitchen table onto the farthest end of the balcony away from the partition, so as not to hear her rat like rustling's.

We eat in silence..... it is nice on the balcony in the evening light. After dark we go up on the roof to look at the stars. He is eager to learn how to find the Pole star for survival techniques. I am able to it point it out, midway between the Plough and Cassiopeia.

"It doesn't help us survive in Athens though does it."

Nothing moving in the kitchen now. Don't dare to hope the battle won. We have certainly decimated the opposition, but they may not be completely routed. Anything moving creates an instant reaction in me. This morning, I slammed my foot on a piece of toast that had fallen on the floor, thinking it was a cockroach. It's automatic.

Pippa rang Sunday night..... "Everything alright?"

"We're fine. Had a bit of trouble with some cockroaches, that's all..." ~~

18.

HOW LONG, O LORD....HOW LONG?

We breakfast in the dawn out on the balcony with Orion on high. Sounds exquisite, as if one should have nothing to complain of. Nature is all right, it is everything else that is wrong. While he is at school, my days are passed like those lived in a hotel bedroom – the epitome of negative living I yawn my way round the supermarket gathering yet another load of essentials, though I try to keep the housekeeping to the minimum to save Pippa's pocket.

It is so hot for September. In the afternoons the kitten and I lie on the bed, side by side, the Kitten stretched out like a dog sleeping.

I am the epitome of the bored, frustrated housewife! Pippa said two weeks. It's a month now. I'm still here..

His bike has been vandalized in the basement of the building where he keeps it with the other kids bikes; both tyres punctured- an insider job. It shows the attitude toward us as 'foreigners'. He brings his bike up into the flat now.

When I came back from shopping, the kitten had managed to wind the bicycle up in a web of cotton from a cotton reel as if an insect has been making a cocoon of it. I leave it for L. to see.

Where are these White refugee Zimbabweans? In desperation I phone Pippa. "When are the people coming?"

"They are flying in from Africa tomorrow. I was just going to ring you."

"Oh – okay..." and put the phone down with no sense of relief, suddenly feeling sad at the idea of abandoning him to strangers again.

He takes the information without visible emotion.

"You put up with an awful lot, Lol..." admiring the way he copes with it, never challenging Pippa's arrangements for him – not out of weakness, but out of strength. He doesn't want to make it difficult for her, the `Koala Bear' he loves most `in the whole wide world. But he is a realist.

"It's a bad arrangement," he shrewdly points out. "Mummy has to pay the rent, but they don't *have* to feed me."

He has experience. He has gone hungry a lot when dependent on other people, but has never complained to Pippa.

I make him up a `Survival Tuck Box' containing iron rations of tins of baked beans, tuna, Dolmades, a couple of packets of spaghetti and some Soya milk, biscuits and chocolate. He has hidden it under his bed, quite relieved to have it. It won't last him long, but is better than nothing.

"I'd better not use it till I'm desperate," he says.

We have got the flat into a state of unseemly tidiness and cleanliness in preparation for the new arrivals.

"I'll be awfully sorry to see you go, Trayzer...." lying on the bed, with the kitten on his chest, bravely prepared to put up with whatever walks in through the door.

Why was I making such a fuss – of course, I would have stayed with him! Now I am hoping they *don't* turn up, and spend an uneasy night on the bed in the hall, waiting for the buzzer to sound, afraid that if I fall into a deep sleep I won't hear it. He sleeps on the balcony in this sleeping bag `to be out of the way'.

Next morning, Saturday, just when I decide to have a bath, the buzzer rings. It is them. I don't know what I was expecting, but I am agreeably surprised at the young woman and small child who come out of the lift. Soft brown hair cut in a fringe and straight sides falling to below the ears. She looks like a nice British girl from a good class boarding school . It must be the Colonial influence.

Having spent 8 hours in the air, she says, "I didn't like to wake you up at 5 o'clock in the morning – so we hung about the airport till 7.30 before taking a taxi here. I know the taxi man over charged." quoting a figure three times what it should have been. "I knew it, but couldn't do anything about it."

She surprises me again by saying, "My other children will be joining us later."

"How many have you got?"

"Only four. twenty-one, seventeen and twelve, and six."

After a cup of coffee, she goes out immediately to locate herself in the neighbourhood, and to shop.

Alone again, Lawrence and I compare impressions. "She seems rather nice...." He calls her `Mrs. Canary'. I see what he means.

"Not as gaudy as a canary – more like a Nightingale —"

"She's going to teach in our school..." he says.

When she comes back, she tells us she has phoned about a house she is interested in renting. "I found out about it before I left Rhodesia."

She already knows about a house for rent?

"It's very near the school. It will save so much in commuting." She is very business like, and moves fast re-orientating herself, even in a foreign country like Greece.

After lunch we take a taxi to go to find the house. It turns out of be a `Spitaki', a cottage among the olive groves still remaining on the edge of the suburbs, where the School is located.

"Oh, this is perfect.... I'm a country bumpkin. I want space around me. I can't stand the idea of a flat. We can have chickens... and grow vegetables. ... even keep a goat perhaps... and its cheap. My husband will be joining us later. bringing the boys – they will also be attending the School. My husband will have to find a job and my eldest... "

I begin to admire her very much. It must be strange being refugees in Greece from an old British Colonial country – but she is up to it. Perhaps it's the old Colonial spirit.

'But what about Lawrence? I thought he was part of the arrangement?"

"He can live with us."

Well, that puts the boot on the other foot. Does Pippa know about this? Anyway it seems a solution that will suit Lawrence, too. He and the six year old are exploring everything around the place. He is very good with younger kids.

Next day, Lawrence drags my bag down into the street to help me get a taxi to the airport. I feel I am leaving him in good hands – after all she has brought up four children.... what is one more.

I had phoned Pippa I was coming. She said she would meet me, but no sign of her at the Airport. Perhaps she has Consular duties to perform. The luggage takes forever to come up , and suddenly she appears. "I'm sorry I'm late, but I been seeing off a pregnant English girl who is escaping from her Greek boyfriend," breathing a quick sigh of relief. "I was afraid he might turn up and make a scene."

"So these are you Consular Duties?"

"Oh, yes – you can't imagine. This man has been married three times, has six children whom he doesn't support, and he was keeping this English girl virtually a prisoner for `safe sex'. I think she has seen the light now. Anyway .... she's gone."

We drive off to the village to be greeted ecstatically by Pickle, Damn Sam. Poxy Percy responds to me, but still looks as if he has a headache.

"I'm having trouble with Pickle. He has taken to chasing chickens. The neighbours are complaining, and demanding money for the chickens he has killed. At first I didn't believe them. I thought they were trying it on, because I'm new to the village, and they don't like dogs as pets.... but looking out of my window one morning I saw him coming up the path with a live chicken in his mouth."

"What's come over him?"

"I don't know. I take him to work most days, but I couldn't this morning because of seeing off that girl. Otherwise he has to be tied up. Any way tell me about the new woman....."

I tell her about the Spitaki in the Olive Grove.

"Sounds good – I can give up the flat and pay her for his keep. Anyway, I am going to send him to England as soon as he finishes at the School. He can live with Ganga and go to the Sixth Form College near her. It's supposed to be very good."

I am dismayed – I thought Athens was far enough. She seems always to be pushing him further away from her, denying herself for his good, though it can't be good for her.......

19.

PET-MINDING

Now I'm back, I hardly see Pippa unless I call in to the Consulate on my way into town, to find her sitting behind her desk in an unostentatious, but thoroughly competent way. She has bought a lot of new clothes to dress the part. Amusing to compare her image now, a steady reliable mature young woman, in smart navy blue jacket and straight skirt, with her younger self; long hair, ethnic skirts, and sandals surrounded by a motley crew of stray animals.

We leave her office together, "I've got to go to the jail. " she says.

I know she visits the hospital when tourists have come to grief from heart attacks, crashing motorbikes or cars, but the *Jail*?

" We have a couple of Brits in for 10 years for drug offences. I take them a sandwich or a pizza, and books to read. "

She also has to organize official Memorial Services at the British Cemetery for Armistice Day, or for British sailors drowned in local waters during the war.

"Will you come to the Anglican Church with me on Sunday? I think I ought to put in an appearance.." She is an Atheist.

" Surely you're not changing your spots?"

"No, of course not, but I have heard on the grapevine that my appointment has `shocked' the Anglican community. So I thought I would put in an appearance."

"But that's silly, the Consulate is not a *Religious* office. "

"To many Brits it would be......"

"Anyway, there's a new vicar. The last one was telling English girls they had sinned by marrying Greeks, and twice sinned having children!"

"Okay...I'll come – it will be an experience."

~~~~~~~~~~~~~~~~

Dear Mummy,

I have been trying to phone you for days. You said you were there in the evenings but I never got you. I have missed you so much.

It rained *kareklo-pthara* yesterday, but I went to school on my bike and it was April Fool's day, but we were too soggy to torment the teachers and it was a shame.

I am feeling terrible I am week and feel cold when it is hot so I think I have got a temperature also my mouth is as dry as rock and my neck is swollen under my ears. Does not matter, I have not missed a day of school yet and I hope it goes away soon. I have not told anyone and I am not going to.

You promised we would go camping when I come home at Easter.

Please write and tell me how you are or phone me. I love you very very much.

Lawrence.
XXXXXXXXXXXXXXXXXXXXXXXXXXXXXXXXXXX LOVE ME

~~~~~~~~~~~~~~~~

She has gone to Athens for a few days to see if he's alright, and go to the Embassy.

I move in to be with the animals, my first time alone here. It feels isolated ,even though it is in a Village. Existing like this in somebody else's space is a curious experience. Time passes very slowly in other people's houses. I never have enough of it in my own. Her other house was an extension of my own existence, but in this space, I feel like a spider moving up and down a gossamer thread in infinite space.

When I went into the kitchen to make tea in the morning, Percy asleep on the little settee in front of the Spanish Main extends his body in a long arabesque, opening his pink mouth in greeting, looking up with his head round the wrong way. He has human eyes. Sometimes he lies on his back with his front paws at his sides, his back legs straight out just like a human. It looks peculiar in a cat. Since we brought him back from Athens, the other animals pretend he doesn't exist. Pippa doesn't take to him either. He has never got over being abandoned in that sterile apartment block in 'Hollow-ghouli-land' and looks as if he has permanent migraine, but I like Percy, that's why he is always glad to see me. There is a sympathy between us .

This morning he was sitting up on the cupboard trying catch Time with his paws on the kitchen clock.

Cat catching time

When I am doing my morning 'Thai Chi ' routine, Percy seems to recognise the Form, springing down from his place on the ironing board, keeps close to my feet as I move, yet without getting in the way. We move together. It's weird. He often interferes with my Yoga, wanting to sit on me when I'm attempting the Lotus position.

I am getting less than my needful amount of sleep as the animals break the night in to fragments using my bed as a trampoline. Percy is no trouble, he sleeps in the kitchen or spends the night outside. Now I put Damn Sam out at night too, but he arrives at my bedroom window by jumping from the ruin beside the house onto the front porch. I wake to find him staring in with his 'Samurai' eyes through the window pane.

I go down to the kitchen to make tea and bring it back upstairs. Having let Sam in, and got back into bed, he jumps onto my chest and settles there, with his face right up to mine, which makes it difficult to drink my tea.

If Pickle jumps aboard Sam stares at him with his mad eyes, quite furious, daring him to come any closer. So Pickle lies along my legs where my hand can tickle him, making it even more difficult to drink my tea.

I weighed Sam on the bathroom scales this morning. 5 kilos! I shall weigh Pickle as well, I want to know the total weight I am supporting.

It is a bore having to take Pickle for a walk on a lead – because of his new penchant for chasing chickens. We go up the path behind the house, that winds up through allotments on to the road above. At the sound of chickens clucking, he stops and peers. "Bad dog – Pickle! What has got into you! " When we get on to the road I let him free. He twinkles along, sniffing at everything – but the moment I stop to look at a flower, or the view, he stops too, waiting impatiently as I stare at some flower or bird. *"What are you looking at?* " He can't enjoy his walk unless I am moving too, yet if he gets a bowel movement, he squats, anxiously fixing me with his eyes. *"Don't leave me.... wait......"* If I walk on, he can't 'go' and coming out of his squat, walking awkwardly " I haven't finished, look what you're making me do....."

When I siesta in the afternoon, he sits by the bed, his eyes gleaming in a certain way among all the hair. Suddenly he jumps up and rolls on top of me. I push him over against the wall where he lies, paws in the air, utterly content, not even demanding to have his tummy tickled.

In the evenings, the animals – in collusion for once – pretend I have not given them any supper.

I take the risk of letting Pickle go for his nightly run on his own, trusting the chickens are all shut up. When he comes back, he follows me up to bed with the impetuousness of a lover. He has wet feet and is forbidden to get up on the bed. He voices his protests, quivering from head to tail with frustration, and goes away.

I put his blanket outside my door and shut it firmly. I hear his paws coming up the stairs again. He reads the message of his blanket outside my door, and weeps audibly. It is all I can do not to give in.

Oh, these animals. Both Sam and Pickle insist on sleeping with me now, not only with me, but on top of me. I have tried keeping them out, but they win in the end. Yet Pippa insists they do not behave like this with her. Then it must be, that without her presence in this house, they feel so insecure, and have to cleave to me. This house is not home to them either, and with Pippa away they cling to me for reassurance. They can hardly bear me out of their sight. I wonder what it is like to keep an orphanage. I wake up finding myself lying diagonally across the bed, with the cat on the pillow and Pickle sleeping across the bottom of the bed.

I came into the kitchen this evening to pour myself another glass of Retsina . Sam is sitting on the top of the plastic bin, with his back towards me. It is a statement : '<u>When</u> are you going to give us our supper?"

Sam sitting on the Bin

Pippa turned up at 10 pm. from the evening plane. Pickle was out. She was disappointed that he wasn't there to greet her. Suddenly a whining and crying at the kitchen door. She leapt up to open it, and Pickle hurled himself at her. That is what she was wanting. She needs the animals in this house as much as they need her.~~

To THE BEST PERSON IN THE WHOLE WIDE WORLD!! 28-4-88

Dear Mummy,

I have tryed to phone you but you Wern't there in the evenings. My pile of bricks for your absenses is geting larger it looks like modern art. How are you , I hope Well. for some reason I can't sleep, last night I only dozed off for at the most two to three minuits. I would look at my clock and it would say 2.10. I would go to sleep for about four hours or so and wake up at 2.13.

It still hurts under my ear but I can still hear through it. I think perhaps I am getting better but I don't know. Do you know my tonge still herts from being so dry but now it is wet again. Oh well, that is a good sign and it makes eating easierYou promised we would go camping again when I come home at Easter.

Hope you are well, how is Pickle send him my love. No need for worry, love Lawrence.

xxxxxxxxxxxxxxxxxxxxx Love me.

PS Love to Trayzer..

20.

CAMPING AT THE ACHERON RIVER

The Easter holiday comes round on the carousel of the year. We go to meet him at the airport. Pippa keeps her promise to go camping. "We're going the Acheron River." She always keeps her promises. "We must get the first ferry in the morning. So get all your stuff together – Lol." She has it all worked out; she wasn't a Tourist Guide for nothing.

Six o'clock in the morning we are ready to set off. It is still dark. Pickle, who has not been informed of our plans, is "Night-wandering" as is his habit now that he is not allowed out alone in the day because of the chickens.

"We *can't* go without Pickle..." Pippa says desperately. "At this rate we are going to miss the Ferry....."

Suddenly, the hairy beast arrives; Lawrence grabs him and throws him into the car. We speed down to the harbour, catch the ferry by the skin of our teeth, and chug across the sea as the dawn fattens above the mainland mountains. Magic.

On the other side, we set off south, traversing a flat zone of an extinct lake, where agriculture is in full swing, watered by huge jets of water. Lawrence wants to stop to steal a few corn cobs for supper.

Where the flatness ends the mountains rise in soft triangles, one behind the other. We cross a Bailey bridge, drive along a track by the side of the river, through olive trees. Suddenly, in front of us, is the ruined pier of an ancient Roman bridge standing in the swirling turquoise water of the river. Further on we come to a grove of plane trees growing in shingle beside the river where it flows out of a narrow gorge. People have camped on the opposite bank under the wall of the ravine. Lawrence is instantly jealous as it is the perfect campsite.

The water in the river is crystal clear, purling along at a fast walking pace; the white pebbles at edge form small beaches. Plane trees grow all along the banks. The sun, striking through the branches creates a sylvan fairy land. We have arrived. Parking the car, we wade thigh deep through piercingly cold the water to get to the other side, and follow a path till it peters out at the beginning of the narrow ravine where the river flows out of the mountains above us. Here we wade into the river again, entering the high walled corridor with trees hanging over us as in Japanese paintings, the dazzling light filtering down into the ravine makes it neither gloomy or forbidding.

From a cave on the left, a tongue of clear water gushes out from the throat of the earth. Water seeps out of the rocky walls entering the river's flow from every nook and cranny, and bubbling up through the water as if from a sunken organ emitting water instead of sound through all its pipes.

Wading up to our thighs again, I was in front because I had kept my shoes on making it easier to walk on the pebbles of river bed. It felt as if one should acknowledge and propitiate the spirit of the place so I started to sing the only sacred song that came to mind, Gounod's *Ave Maria*, I sang at full throttle. The others didn't tell me to shut up. After all, my mother was an opera singer and the acoustics, like a bathroom, made it impressive. It seemed right.

But the water was icy cold; we turned back, though with reluctance, and laid ourselves out on the shingle in full sun to warm us.

Pippa fell asleep instantly like a princess in a fairy tale. Lawrence hung his army belt carrying his precious army knife, in a tree above her head, and roamed about picking up pebbles. I lay on my back looking up through the leaves and suddenly saw a butterfly land on Lawrence's Army belt. It was a 'Two Tailed Pasha'! I had seen Silver Washed Fritillaries, a Clouded Yellow; we had seen a Kingfisher, but a Two Tailed Pasha, – so appropriate to this area, once ruled over by the infamous Ali Pasha, the Sadaam Hussein of Epirus.

Suddenly, we heard the noise of a motorbike. A motorbike? Here? A boy on a motorbike appeared at the other bank and drove his bike straight into the river. The inevitable happened, the engine flooded. He sat on the bike in the middle of the river, trying to start it.

Lawrence watched in silent contempt.

There was nowhere on our side of the river where he could ride the bike but he pushed it across on to the little pebble beach near us and tried monotonously to start it again.

"That boy is *An Idiot*.," said Lawrence.

"If I had had a gun I would shoot him!" I say, "and claim it as justifiable homicide!" incensed at having *that* noise in *this* place.

The boy sat on the beach until the hot sun dried out the engine, when he started it again. drove it up and down the tiny beach, showing off, because we were there even though we ignored him. Then he pushed it back across the river, and had to wait for it to dry out again on the other side.

"He doesn't understand *anything*," says Lawrence. Machines are like animals to him – to be treated properly.

To me it shows the truth of that statement about Nature `where every prospect pleases and only man is vile'.

Pippa slept through the whole incident. Sleep is the great escape for her. She needs it. When she woke, the first thing she said was, "Where's Lol?" He had disappeared. We waded back across the river and found him at our camp. He had erected the two tents. (I had my own tent now) and laid the fireplace with specially selected flat stones.

The light was removing itself from the gorge by this time though it was only the middle of the afternoon. We brewed up tea with water from the river – it was so pure.

The camp on the other bank lit their fire. Its presence across the river was companiable without being intrusive. Cracks of gunfire ricocheted above us making a fearful din.

A large tractor came bouncing along the shingle toward our camp site, towing a trailer filled with metal pipes. The driver stopped right between our camp and the river. The two men got down, obviously a father and son. Apart from a nod, and the basic greeting, they said not a word as lifting the pipes from the trailer, laid them within a foot of our camp fire to a field of maize behind us. Luckily our tents were not in the way. They proceeded to pump water from the river into this patch of land for 1½ hours.

"So much for the peace one only finds in Nature....." I suggest.

They sat on the stones near us and after a while, began to ask questions very politely and with dignity, not with a vulgar curiosity in strangers. These mountain people are courteous and nice.

The kids from the camp across the river, had devised a game, riding their airbeds in the river. Lawrence was filled with jealousy. "Mummee....."

"No, Lol, you can't put my airbed in the river. I've got to sleep on it... it will be all wet. We can't dry it now."

At last the two men gathered up their water pipes, loaded them and the pump onto the trailer and bounced away; the kids across the river had given up their sport – at last we could hear the sound of the river again. We made a supper of roasted sausages and the corncobs Lol had stolen from the maize field; only he could gnaw at them with his strong young teeth as they must be grown for animal fodder. After washing our teeth in the river, (unique experience), we crawl into our tents tired and happy.

I never expect to sleep well in a tent; I kept waking every 2 hours. At 5 a.m., I was puzzled by a shadow , like the Hanging man, lying across the fabric of the tent, and crawled out to find the whole of the grove saturated in moonlight with Orion pegged out just above the cliff face. There *are* advantages to not being able to sleep in a tent.

I went to the camp fire. It was out, so I started gathering sticks in the moonlight. Lawrence had left the matches by the fire [black mark for bad camp craft]. I felt like a Stone Age woman, absorbed in trying to get the fire to burn, nurturing the little fingers of flame. I scooped water from the river to boil tea, grateful that in this age of pollution, this river could be trusted.

The others slugged abed in their tent. Then I heard her moan, "I'm on the stones, Lol..."

Her airbed had gone down in the night even though Lawrence had patched it in three places before we came away.

"It doesn't matter...." from Lol.

"It does, Lol...."

As I wait for the water to boil I watch the light as the sun began to probe fingers down into the gorge until the whole canyon was radiant. I call out to them "Don't miss this! Pippa! Lol! You've got to see this!" full of excitement. It was like tackling a scorpion.

"It's not the time for sightseeing...." she growls.

"But you must see it in this light!"

"I'll see it later...."

I don't try again. I've learned my lesson.

When Pippa and Lol emerge, we make an enormous breakfast of eggs, and bacon, and wash the plates and cups in the river. Quite time consuming, but what had Time to do with it. We were in the Timeless Zone, washing our plates in the River of Immortality.

Suddenly we see the goats high on the rim of the cliffs. About a hundred goats, hopping and skipping from ledge to ledge, descend what to us looks like a wall of rock to the river, where they stay grazing and resting in the shadows of the Plane trees. Magnificent creatures with glossy black coats and elegant horns. The Bellwethers with huge clanking copper bells on their necks which set up a gamelan orchestra augmenting the continuous sweet burble of the river.

I discover an old fallen plane tree with knobbly trunk forming an arch like a bridge framing the sunlit vista of the goats grazing among the shrubs on the shingle. I sit down to sketch it. As the herd moves toward me, I sit very still; munching and farting they eye me with pagan eyes, and choose to ignore me.

I watch, mesmerized, as a big Bellwether clambers up into the fallen tree with the insolent grace of a gypsy, to forage on the leaves. She peers down at me, her head framed by the leaves – a Pagan Spirit. I sketch her too – the essence of the non-Christianized world. *'There was a golden Age – who murdered it?'*

Goat up the tree

As the day wore itself away, we waded and swam – or attempted to swim in the icy waters. Lawrence managed a brief swim. Pippa and I dunked ourselves very quickly like ducks and came up gasping, – then lay out on the warm pebbles to recover, watching the turquoise and aquamarine water, as it twirled and eddied by in slow and fast streams, lulled by its perpetual babble, mesmerized by the swirling patterns on its surface. In a deep green shaded pool were terrapins. We sat there gazing and listening to the river with foolish expressions of happiness on our faces, and no need of speech. It was Tao.

The other campers had packed their things and gone, leaving us in sole possession of the place – for one more night, to our slight apprehension and great joy. We waded across the river to examine their camping spot. "We will come here next time – won't we, Mumm-ee...." says Lawrence.

As the afternoon waned, the goats began to ascend the wall of the gorge by a different route. It was a very orderly retreat – the Bellwethers standing sentinel at strategic points watching out for any stragglers among the kids who bleated when they found themselves isolated. It was better organised than the retreat of an army. Then we heard the shrill whistle of the shepherd who had come to meet them on the heights above us, probably having driven to the nearest point in his car. It was surprising that these independent creatures accept man's dominion over them.

"Perhaps they know it is to their advantage to have a secure shelter for the night....." There are wolves in these parts, and bears and wild boar.

When we crawled into our tents we were quite alone in the gorge – the only human life there, without even a mosquito for company.

In the early morning the moon painted a "Matisse" on the side of my tent . Crawling out into the moon-silvered grove, I found the ashes of our fire still glowing, and set about reviving it with dry sticks. What an experience – *a dream which exceeds the dream* because it is real.

It was ages before the other two surfaced. The long holiday weekend was over, but not quite for us. Lawrence was doing what he had longed to do after seeing those other kids. He had Pippa's airbed in the river – having a grand time surfing along, then carrying it back up stream to do it again... and again.

Pippa and I sat on the shingle silently watching the flow of water. It had so many different tempos. The ambitious stream, fast and shallow, the still waters which run deep, the ambling water, and water that crashed into everything in its path, water meandering in devious routes around obstacles, regaining the mainstream in its own time. It was analogous with life.

"In Herman Hess's novel about Buddha, he says that when he understood the voice of the river he was freed from the conflict of desires. it was OM......"

"Umm...." said Pippa.

We did not want to leave the place, but our withdrawal was assisted by an incident. We could hear a bulldozer just around the corner from our camp, chewing noisily at the rocks accompanied by the sound of pneumatic drills, but lulled by the sense of peace the river gave, we ignored it

Then I waded over to the ideal campsite to sketch the trees. On my way back across the river – suddenly there was a human shout like a logger's warning cry, followed immediately by an explosion. I was mid-river, up to my thighs gawking at a pinky orange mushroom-shaped cloud like a miniature atom bomb. Rocks and stones splashed down into the water in front of me and into the trees near the camp where Pippa was cooking lunch with a frying pan in her hand.

A man came running through the trees shouting "Get out of here!" But it was too late. By the grace of the Gods, the stones missed us – even the car was undamaged.

I was all for beating a hasty retreat in case of another detonation, but Pippa pointed out that suddenly there was no more sound from the bulldozer or the pneumatic drill.

"This is an official camp site. They should have checked the grove was empty after the Bank Holiday weekend. They are scared they have killed some tourists in the trees. They've panicked and gone. They always do."

So we had our lunch, packed up the car and drove back to Igoumenitza.

We arrive to find "An Abandonment of the Harbour" in progress, i.e. a strike. Queues, people, heat, frustration; but the protest was against the pollution of the river by chemical waste from new factories at Jannina, which would affect the whole coast, the fishing, and the beaches .

So we all settled down to sweat it out. After only a couple of hours, we found ourselves on a ferry chugging back towards our island thoroughly satisfied with our excursion. The only one who hadn't enjoyed the experience was Pickle. Dogs do not like camping. ~~

I don't get to see him much during the rest of the holiday, she makes him study.

"It's for the best , Lol."

There is new emphasis on him getting enough grades to make him eligible for the English school. He will finish in Athens at the end of the year.

I remember when he was six sitting at the table , weeping, "I'll never be finished with BLOODY HOMEWORK now..." He doesn't want to disappoint her though.

She says she will send him to England to finish his schooling.

"There is a Sixth Form College near Mum. He can live with her, and go there.... I've told mother to investigate it. It is supposed to be very good...."

When the time comes round on the carousel again, we see Lol off at the airport, watching him lope across the Tarmac with many a turn to wave, until he is absorbed into the capsule of the aircraft. Pippa is transformed at these moments, a broad grin clamped across her mouth, full of pride and emotion she will not let herself express. ~~

23.

TOSCA

I call in on Pippa at the Consulate on my way into town to find workmen erecting a counter and protective screen across the wide hall, to separate the staff from the public. At the moment anybody can walk straight in to her office.

"With recent bomb scares in Athens and attacks on other Embassies, they say we have to have it."

But there is still no barrier between Pippa and animals.

"Come and look at this...." leading me into the corridor where, out of a cardboard box, totters a long legged spindly puppy, black, white and tan markings.

"She tottered in to the road right in front of the car when I was driving in to work... .isn't she a poppet!"

"She was lucky it was you, or she would have been jam. What are you going to do with it?"

"Oh, I'll find a home for her. Fotios says he wants a dog...."

Fotios is the old man who owns the front half of the house. and lives in the bottom of it. He had two wives both died on him, without giving him children, so he is all alone. He's a stalwart character, very independent, looking after himself. He used to have a horse and cart to transport things out to the village. He enjoys having Pippa in the other half of the house. She brings him a newspaper from town everyday.

The pup, loving the attention, wavers about in front of us in an ecstasy of humility and gratitude, looking as fragile as a Geisha girl.

"Come up next weekend," she says suddenly.

'I'll be on standby, so we won't be able to do much.'

I accept. It seems funny to be invited now – so different from the old days.

"Meet me outside the Courthouse about 1.30. I've got a couple of cases on , but should be finished by then. I can give you a lift."

"Okay, fine........"

Pippa emerges from the Courthouse holding a file in her arms followed like lambs by the Tourists she is helping. She pauses to reassure them. They look loathe to be parted from her.

``So those are your parishioners..." as we walk to the car. "Who are they and what's the matter with them?"

"English chaps from Liverpool. They were arrested for using bad language, aggressive behaviour and fouling corridors in the place they are staying. They swear they have done nothing of this – on the contrary the Greek who owns the rooms was forever creeping around at night, opening their doors with a pass key hoping to catch them with girls. He threatened them with a gun for coming in late and making too much noise. So they are taking out charges against him for the same charges he is taking out against them!"

"I don't know how you cope with it. It must be your love of animals that makes you able to deal with them"

Driving back, she says, "The pup has got distemper."

"Oh will you have it put down?"

"No, I'll try to give her a chance...."

She spends the next days nursing it, giving it intensive care, taking it up to bed with her. The pup loved it. It was bliss to be carried up and down the stairs, to sleep by the bed – thoroughly spoiled – it knew how to make the best of it.

Pip, on Standby for the Consulate, has to stay home by the telephone. The emergencies were coming in. She was on the phone talking to a chap in prison – guiding him through his problems like a Universal Aunt, just the right degree of involvement and detachment so the person feels she is doing all she can for them.

She has plenty of tales to tell . "I had one little fellow who was convinced he was being chased all over the island by twelve Scotsmen.. He had been to the a Police Station They contacted me."

"So what could you do? "

"I persuaded him to come with me to the Crazy House, telling him he would be safe there from the 12 Scotsmen. Then I had to ring his parents to tell them. They didn't seem to realise he had a problem at all. He is 23 and still lives at home. This year is the year of the nut-cases. In the same week I had an English chap dancing nude along the Arcade in town."

"In front of the cafes? How do you deal with that?" full of admiration.

The phone rang again. She picked it up, her face registering shock. "I will have to ring you back – I haven't received any notification yet. I am very sorry."

She put the phone down, looking white. "That was a woman phoning from England. She said `I've just been told my son has been killed."

She set about phoning the Aliens Police and the hospital. Yes – an English boy had been killed on a scooter that morning. Pippa sat quietly for a moment before picking up the phone to dial England. When she put it down again, "The woman said *`but he was speaking to me on the phone this morning at 8 o'clock. He said he was fine and having a wonderful time.* "

She was silent for a moment, "I was talking to Lol this morning....

The puppy survived the distemper, though ever after had a compulsive spasm in the her right foreleg, and became the bobbing dog.

"The Vet says she must never have pups. It would kill her. Her kidneys would give out. "

I can't remember how she came to be called `Tosca', I think I had something to do with it. I felt she was a bit of a Prima Donna; the name stuck.

When the summer holidays come round, Pippa makes me understand that she wants Lol to herself, so I won't be moving up there when he comes. I understand., but miss the sound of his sandals flapping down my path.

"But I must see him before he goes again...."

"Of course!" she says.

24.

Eventually I get up to the village for his last weekend. Lol was in the kitchen making himself a snack.

"That's the biggest sandwich I've ever seen!"

"No, Trayzer – this is small...."

Pippa disappears for a siesta. "I have to meet the Viennese Ambassador this evening...."

He and I are on our own just like in Hollow-Ghouli-land. And he says, "Trayzer – do you know that cave up there?"

"What cave?"

From the front porch he points up the steep hillside to a dark spot on the rock face. "Shall we go up there?"

"It looks awfully high... well – okay ," I would go anywhere with him. "Why not?"

Next thing I know, I am climbing through dense thicket, following his lithe form. "Have you been up here before?"

"Yes, I did it when I first came back."

It gets steeper and steeper. He has to haul me up over a drystone wall. The strength in his arm is potent.

"Hang on a minute. I need a rest!" I say, sitting down amongst the dense undergrowth. Suddenly, an emerald green beetle comes walking toward us like a jewel on legs. "Oh, look at that!" as it goes on its way impervious of our presence.

He has to give me another heave to get me up , but eventually we get to the cave, and sit looking out over the island like a pair of buzzards. "Oh, Lol – only you can give me experiences like this!" so grateful to him.

"Really , Trayzer?"

"Yes – sleeping in dustbin bags. Only you can do this for me."

As usual, going down is worse than coming up, but we get back to the house, where I have a celebratory Ouzo and start cooking dinner. Suddenly he says, "You can do the splits, can't you, Trayzer. I remember you said you could."

"When I was a kid – yes – I could tie myself in knots. "

"How do you do it?" It is his ambition to do the splits?

With another Ouzo, I cautiously discover – I can still do the splits!

"That's really good, Trayzer!"

"I should say it is – at my age!"

"You're not old, Trayzer."

"That's because you always make me behave like a kid!"

Too soon we are seeing him off at the airport.

"Do work hard Lol – to get your grades.... It is important." she urges him.

We watch him lope toward the aircraft , turning to wave before he ducks into the plane.

25.

CHRISTMAS

"We won't be going to England for Christmas this year," she says. "It will be the first Christmas in the new house, just the three of us. A Vegetarian Christmas." taking down the vegetarian cookbook. "I shall do a Lentil and mushroom roast."

Lawrence's prime Christmas present is a first-rate Sleeping bag, and Bivouac blanket from Grandpa. "Mummy – we can sleep on the mountain."

"Brrr.... It will be cold up there! It's winter. " She doesn't like sleeping anywhere except her own warm bed.

"But my sleeping bag is for minus zero temperatures."

"That's great for you. What about us?"

"But I can make us special beds – you won't be on the ground...."

He is disappointed at our lack of enthusiasm.

"Why don't you try it out yourself on the hill above the house..." I suggest. "It's wild and rough enough up there." He takes up the idea immediately "I can make a bed like the one in the Survival book. Look! It's really excellent, Trayzer...." showing me the diagram of two posts tied together in the form of an X on which you suspend a bed made like a stretcher on two poles. "But I'll need some stuff for the mattress." Pippa comes back from town with a roll of plastic Hessian. "Will this be any good?" He spends all day on the hill above the house making his camp bed, while I have the job of stitching the stuff together to make the mattress so he can slot two poles down the sides.

After supper I escort him up to the place where he has made his bed. Pickle has to come too, and Sam the cat.

The bed was simple and effective. "That looks great, Lol."

He shows me how he can fix up his emergency Bivvy blanket to form a tent over the bed, and crept into his brand new sleeping bag. "It's good isn't Trayzer." "It certainly is!"

Poor Pickle is very dubious when he is lashed to the bedstead and not allowed to follow me home, and whines pitifully thinking , probably, how he was allowed to share my duvet. From the sublime to the bizarre.... I give him a hug and wrap him the blanket we brought for him. Then I have to leave them to stumble down the steep way, accompanied by Mad Sam dancing crazily all over the place like a Djinn.

In the morning when I heard the hunters banging off, I hoped they wouldn't put a bullet through his Bivvy. I hadn't thought of the hunters. Who would suspect a boy sleeping out up there? I went up the hill early taking him cake and cocoa. Pippa was soundly sleeping off the effects of the party.

I found him in his Bivvy bed with poor Pickle lying on top of him for warmth and comfort. Lawrence was in a state of bliss. "It's every so nice...Trayzer. You ought to try it..."

It was so beautiful on the hillside in the early morning . He talked of the brilliance of the stars, I was envious... perhaps I ought not to pass over the experience.. while my stock lasts....

An old woman and her goats suddenly appeared, and was as surprised to see us as we were to see her. She said she owned the land, and asked if he was in the Boy Scouts. Quite a sensible interpretation. It makes him decide to remove his bed and remake it higher up the steeply sloping hill. "I could make a bed for you too Trayzer."

So I sew another mattress while he spends hours perfecting the new campsite. It was dark when he came down.

New Year's Eve. Pippa has to go to a New Year's Eve Party. "I hate the New Year...always have done, since I was a child." "Why?" asked Lol, to whom Time means nothing. "Brrr..." she shivered. "I just do..." and walked out of the kitchen in a very grouchy mood for her, leaving us to make our supper and go up the hill to our camp.

Lawrence cooked our supper of rice – as part of his survival technique. It was very good. I lit the candles on the table and with this night in front of me, had two dry martinis. They jacked me up for the scramble up the steep hillside in the dark. I had my sleeping bag, and a pure wool rug, my Balaclava (from our Hymettos days), my new country weather coat, long johns under my track suit, thick socks. After all, I am not a novice. Even so, it wasn't easy to get up the rocky pathless hillside in the dark. Lawrence carried the rest of the gear and pulled the reluctant Pickle on his lead.

The two beds he had made were really excellent in design. Cross poles lashed together at head and foot. Poles slotted through the plastic sacking I had diligently sewn, made the stretcher which rested on the bases of the crossed poles. He had contrived a pole across the top of the beds to support the Bivvy blanket, or a bit of plastic sheeting for me, making the whole thing into a tent.

"This is much better than dustbin bags." insinuating myself fully dressed into my non-survival cotton sleeping bag. With the tent flap thrown back I found myself looking straight up at a sky blazing with stars.

"What a way to spend the last Night of the Year!" thrilled by the experience already.

From our beds we studied the stars for a while. I had brought my planisphere. He had to read it because he had the torch. But I could recognise Orion, and Sirius... "those two over there are Castor and Pollux.."

Pickle bedded down on a blanket with an aluminium sheet over him, seemed resigned this time – perhaps my presence was reassuring.

Lol and I say goodnight and lower our flaps. Sleep does not come. I give up trying. I am fairly comfortable but bored, and open my flap again to watch the stars. I must have slept a bit, but not enough to notice. At Midnight – *All Hell let loose!* Guns going off all over the hills in every direction. Hooters blaring, two red flares hung over the harbour far away. Shot from a nearby gun peppered down all around us.

"Hey! What's going on?" says Lawrence coming to. He had been fast asleep. "It's the beginning of a New Year." "So what?"

he says, snuggling back into his bag. Children have no sense of time.

> *When I was a child I slept and wept – Time crept*
> *When as a youth I laughed and talked – Time walked.*
> *When I became a full grown man – Time ran*
> *And older as I daily grew – Time flew*
> *Soon I shall be travelling on – Time gone....*

I didn't try to sleep, watching my sign of Leo in the sky above me all night long. Poor Pickle, cold and damp whimpered and whined. My sleeping bag became wet from condensation, but I was snug enough in my padded coat and pure wool rug. *There is no substitute for wool.* The top of my Balaclava was wet too, but I could breathe warm air through the face piece.

I slept quite deeply toward the end of the night. When I woke I was relieved to see the progress the stars had made. The horns of a waning moon had risen over the mainland mountains. Spectacular sight. Leo was well to the West now, the Plough had raised its question mark. In the Dawn, the Morning Star was like a diamond. The night was over.

I was surprised when Lol's voice said, "Shall I go down and make us some Cocoa?" "Brilliant idea." He went down the hill in leaps and bounds. In no time he was back carrying two mugs and the coffee percolator full of hot sweet cocoa.

I was standing watching the sky lighten, still in my Balaclava, padded coat with the rug wrapped round my legs like a skirt- lost in the mystery of the Cosmic Being ....or something....

"Trayzer – I don't think you should go out in the street like that..." I hear his voice saying in all seriousness.

"What?" rudely dragged back to earth from the Cosmic mystery to the reality of my appearance in the eyes of another. (my appearance on camping nights has always embarrassed him.)

"I just think you shouldn't wear a skirt with a Balaclava."

"I didn't come up here to win a Beauty contest!"

The hot cocoa was delicious, but my appearance had made him querulous. While I enthused over the beauty of the sunrise. "Look how big the sun is.!"

Trayzer on the Hillside

"It's always the same size – It cannot be bigger..."
"It *looks* bigger from up here!" exasperated at his obtuseness. "And look at that sausage of steam" A strange bolster of steam seemed to lie on the surface of the sea....
"It can't be steam," he says, "It's cloud." determined to negative everything I say.

I gather myself together, stuffing my gear into the backpack, and descend the hill, more difficult going down than coming up, but I have survived once again. Pippa is still in bed. I light the kitchen stove. Another year is upon us.

This time when we see him off, it is to England. As we come away from the airport, she says,"By the way, Pickle is missing. We haven't seen him for three days. Lol didn't keep him tied up. He didn't realise. I have asked all over the village, nobody says anything but Foti says Pickle was seen chasing the Butcher's sheep. I think...." she doesn't finish. Her favourite dog – the only one of the old guard we had left ~~.

26.

TIG

Walked to town, called in at the Consulate to see Pippa. She is still in a depression. She has been like this since Lawrence went to England. The change in her is alarming. I have never seen her like this. She seems diminished in stature. She is only 5ft 3, but her aura is so positive she appears larger than she is physically. Now her face is set, she cannot smile, even her hair looks dull, though she washes it almost every day. She is like someone struggling with a grief; she has lost her child. She has the status job, the status home, car – but without him – there's nothing really. He is further away than he was in Athens. Not so easy to pop on a plane and see him if only for 24 hours. She knows she will hardly see him from now on. It makes a bleak landscape….and the loss of Pickle doesn't help. A void is opening up with nothing to put in it. She has reached an end, as he has reached a new beginning.

She will weather it and come through, but at the moment it isn't easy to talk to her…. I come away –

The nearer it gets to when she will being going to England to see with him, she cheers up. "Come up the house, if you want this weekend. We can go for a walk. I've got to pick up my new dog from the Library this evening. Come to town, we'll go together."

"Funny place to pick up a dog, isn't it?"

"The woman librarian keeps a refuge for stray dogs…."

The library is housed in the side court of the Palace built by the British.

"I used to come to this place to borrow English books 25 years ago. The girl used to stand in the room as if I were going to steal the books. I read some very strange books – things one would never read unless one is desperate. It was interesting, though.."

I was surprised when the woman in charge was the same girl – now middle-aged and dressed entirely in black. In the gloom beside her desk, sit two old ladies, hands folded patiently in their laps. She introduces her mother and her aunt. It is obvious she has never married. The dog we have come to collect is tied to a chair looking bored and resigned.

"This is my new dog...." Pippa says, bending down to stroke the rough haired mongrel bitch, who feebly wags her tail.

" Another bitch?" I query.

"She's been spayed. She'll be no trouble."

It is quite an attractive animal, though the hairy head doesn't seem to go with the rest of its body. Pippa will always go for the eccentric in an animal.

The dog is ready enough to come with us, to accept it's fate and make the best of it.

Back at house, Tosca bobs towards us like a some kind of animated clown.

"She's pregnant, "Pip says.

"I thought you said she must never have pups!"

"I know – I did my best. When she came on heat I took her to the office every day, until the strays started trying to come into the Consulate. Then I shut her in the cellar, under here..." indicating the kitchen floor, where Lol's workshop is. " I thought she would be safe enough, while I was out – it has bars across the window. When I came back from the office, a great big dog was in there with her. I can't think how he squeezed between the bars. There are no dogs in the village except mine, I can't imagine where he came from."

"Didn't you say her kidneys would give out if she got pregnant?" regarding the animal with the swollen belly, who looked far from giving up the life she so much enjoyed.

"The vet said so.... but she seems alright. I think/hope she has them before I go to England."

"I hope so too.!" The idea of having to be a midwife appalls me. "I have no qualities for the birthing business."

The new dog looked around the kitchen in a resigned way. Tosca growled at it.

"Bad dog! You've got to be friends." Pippa reproves her. She kowtows immediately.

"I think I'll call her Tig," she said. "Tig?"

The new dog looks up as if to say, `I'll answer to anything.'

"Yes, she has a kind of adolescent look."

Tig she remained.

Tig

27.

DOG-SITTING

"Tosca has just given birth," Pippa says, as I walk into the kitchen to take up my duties as Dog-sitter while she is away. "The Vet's here to put them down. I'm keeping one....."

Tosca is bedded down in the corner on a rug with her one, enjoying the attention surrounding her at this moment of time.

"What if she dies on me?" remembering what the Vet had said.

"I've left the vet's number on the table – he's just injecting the other pups outside in the alley. He'll come out if you have problems."

On leaving the kitchen to go to the airport, she manages to save a Gecko, from Poxy Percy. It loses it's tail, and is comatose with shock, but she puts him up on the shelf among the oil lamps. As she disappears down the steps, she tosses back " You may find the animals a bit messy… they've got into some bad habits…. Bye!"

The moment she is gone, Tosca decides it is too cold for her and her pup on the floor, the only place for her is the armchair in front of the kitchen range and insists on getting up into it, holding the pup in her mouth.

"Wait a minute – you're all messy !" looking for an old beach towel to put on it.

She stands by the chair the pup dangling from her jaws, saying with her eyes, *"Oh, do buck up. I can't stand here forever."* Then settles herself comfortably. *"It is the best place, you know – for a nursing mother…."*

Tosca holding puppy in her mouth

My first day has been active. I have hardly sat down. I sawed wood for the stove. Took my needle to the unfinished divan cover in the sitting room which Pippa made , but didn't quite finish a problematic corner. Everything in the house is so nice now, I cannot accept this unfinished tag end. I cobble it together so it looks respectable. I feel it has been waiting for me.

It is bloody cold. I had the stove alight most of the day, but it gives no spectacular heat. The kitchen is a large area. I got it up to 11°C. which is normal for me. I tried drying apple rings in the slow oven.

I am sleeping in Lol's bed upstairs, where there is a bit of a view, though the only real view is from Pip's bedroom next door. But when I looked out of the window at 6 in the morning, the full moon was poised between the fingers of the great cypresses on the hillside above the house, balancing like a ball on the rim of the mountain. Mist filled the valley floor, making islands of the hills. Morning dawned a rather vulgar pink.

Coming down to the cold kitchen, the Gecko is alive and active, splayed out on the white-washed wall, the freckled transparent body and black boot button eyes, graceful even without a tail.

Tig is sprawled comfortably on the Habitat settee, and Tosca curled up in armchair by the stove with the pup. And in front of the fridge is a lake of pee with islands of poo in it. I hit the roof.

"WHAT IS THE MEANING OF THIS!"

They look at me and yawn. *"But we always do it – we can't hold out all night you know. Pippa doesn't mind."* I remember now Pippa saying as she went through the door, `You may find them a bit messy…" A *bit* messy?

I drag them off their beds and rub their noses in it. "Don't you DARE do that again!" They seem surprised at my attitude.

Left to myself in a rain sodden village, I take stock. No potatoes, no rice. What does she eat even on a perpetual diet? I have brought chicken and fish with me – but have nothing to go with it except onions.

I try to light the stove with the remains of a box of matches chewed by a dog. No lighters around, (Pippa doesn't smoke), and the new gas stove has automatic ignition. No kindling wood... paper damp. Result: smoke and failure.

Sunday morning early, the hunters start letting off they blunderbusses on the hill above the house; pellets rain down on the roof. You would think they were after pigs with wings, or flying elephants, but all they shoot are Tits, Robins, and Thrushes. It is a long time since they needed to supplement their diet with wild-life. Now they dress up in expensive SAS gear, have repeater rifles and guns that sound like bazookas.

I get some relief from drawing a cartoon:

The Hunters

`Our brave hunters defending the village from aerial attack from Pigs with wings and airborne elephants. Never in the realm of human conquest has so much been owed by so many, to so few...."

~~~~~~

I hear people attending the church below the house. The day begins to look rather long. It is forecast to rain for 2 days, that means no dry kindling for the stove, so take Tig up the path behind the house to collect sticks for the stoves. Coming down the path again which leads directly to the back of our house, I meet one of the female neighbours. She is most often wheeling a wheelbarrow full of bricks – man's work, but today she was dressed in her Sunday clothes, her face glowing with make-up. She greets me pleasantly but her eyes fix on my boots, my stick and the kindling under my arm. To be dressed like this on a Sunday pinpoints my foreign eccentricity.

Monday, I go down the village to get fresh bread. The boot-faced girl serves me without a civil word making me feel like an alien from another planet. I don't belong to this village. The only people who recognise my existence, are Fotios, the dear old man who lives in the front of the house, and *Kyria* Rhoda who sold the house to Pippa. She greets me warmly. Other than that, I am totally alone except for the mad menagerie.

Time passes slowly in this house on my own. By 10.45 am. I'm already exhausted having used up my energy chasing Tig, who has brought a soiled baby's nappy into the sitting room. Anything nasty and dirty has a fascination for her. She brings in dead birds, and dead or dying kittens. Tosca is sick on the Flokati rug. Plopping it off the rug onto newspaper, almost makes me sick. Tig has taken one of my slippers – can't find it. *Cross.*

The house is cold; 6° in the kitchen, it's warmer outside in the sun. Decide to light the stove in the sitting room; it warms the bedroom above it. It stays warm there through the day whereas the kitchen is like a refrigerator.

At supper the animals all go for each other's plates. Tosca woofs hers quick and goes for Tig's plate, Tig goes for the Sam's, and Sam tries to steal my supper. It is chaos.

Woke at 4. am. Went downstairs to make hot milk and honey. The animals start milling about hopefully. Trudge back to bed, shut them firmly out of my room. Hear them tumbling about playing like children..

Fall asleep, dream I had broken the electric kettle.. Woke to a sulphurous morning light through the window, with rain, and thunder. Question mark: what to do with this day? Coming downstairs, find one of the dogs has pee-ed on the carpet as I forbade them to do it on the kitchen floor. They are so logical. Rub both their noses in it, but suspect the real culprit is Tosca, the bobbing dog. She flops whenever attacked and becomes supinely subservient. `*I can't help it... I'm not all right, you see. It's not my fault... and I'm a nursing mother....*"'

It is almost impossible to manhandle her out of the house, because she goes all floppy. She's a cunning one. This is her second faux pas in 24 hours. My aggression is roused. I grab her by the scruff and fling her through the door. `Go and do it outside!" she bobs off down the alley – "*You're not being nice to me – but I won't hold it against you....*".

As there is nothing to do with the day, I decide to make a cake – using the oranges in the bowl on the table. They turn out to be rotten, with no juice. I can't get the lid off the brown sugar jar. – and it is still only 11.30 a.m. Too early to take to drink.

Find my lost slipper. It has been chewed but not entirely destroyed. It's still raining. Take to drink.

'Damn Sam', the cat, establishes his nullifying weight on me whenever I sit down. By looking so comfortable, it requires an act of cruelty to dislodge him, and it prevents me getting another glass of wine – but I *will*. His white hairs have worked their way into my black jersey. Tig, who is easily bored, starts to chew the light flex to the standard lamp. Shout! I turn into a monster, shouting at the dogs, rubbing their noses in their sins, kicking them out of my bedroom and out of the house.

I went off to bed early. What a night! About 3 a.m. Damn Sam starts picking at my bedroom door, I refuse to let him in. I can't be pegged down under 5 kiloes of cat. I lie there trying the block out the sound of him trying pick the lock. His frustration culminates in his hurling himself against the door. This is intolerable! I capitulate and let him in. He takes up centre of the bed with satisfaction. He even snores while I get no sleep at all.

I try to think what could be a suitable inducement to do this job for the three weeks when she goes away at Christmas. No money, jewels or a free Safari trip could compensate for being at the mercy of her horrible new menagerie! These animals are not the same as dear old Paddy, Pickle, Nellie and Sofi and Koko .

The relief for all of us, when Pippa walks through the door. The animals welcome her with joy, though glancing in my direction their eyes say: *She hasn't been very nice to us, you know – but we'll forgive her.*

28.

MRS. SMITH

Summer comes round on the carousel of the year. Pippa rushed up to my pad to bring me a birthday present of a very nice T-shirt. She looks tired and under strain. She admitted to "Social commitments at night and rushing about looking for lost tourists all day."

"Can't you stay a bit.."

"I really can't – I'm on duty. We are looking for a woman who walked out of a hotel at 7.30 in the morning and hasn't been seen since. That was five days ago. The police are looking for her. I have to keep her husband informed."

As she went off down the stairs, "Don't forget Lol's coming on Friday..."

Friday, the day he is due to arrive, she says, "I'm up to my eyeballs in Mrs. Smith. They would find her today, wouldn't they!" heaving one of her sighs when she is stressed. "Will you meet Lol. I've got to go and get the husband, bring him to the Police station to identify her glasses, then take him to view the body! It's still under a bush. I'll have to drop you off at the airport. I don't know when I'll get free."

She drops me off the Airport. "Explain to Lol....."

He lopes off the plane, looking like an army recruit just emerged from the Barber's.

"Do you like it?" rubbing both hands over his bare scalp. "It needs trimming again – it's too long...."

When he was a kid he had thick blonde hair, and hated having it cut, making such a fuss when Pippa got at it with the scissors to it, crying out as if it were really painful. One always expects the same child to come back. He changes yet remains quintessentially himself.

"Where's Mum?"

"She is doing her Consular duty – having to look at a dead body which has been 13 days under a bush....."

"That's really cool....."

"I don't think she thinks it cool...."

We sit on the grass outside the airport to wait for her to show up. He tells me of his experiences with the Outward Bound Course. "It was really excellent, Trayzer. We did hiking, canoeing, camping and rock dancing..."

"Rock Dancing?"

"Yeah... it was great – and the pot-holding and jumping over the `grotpot"

"What's a Grotpot?"

"It's a pool of slime, Trayzer. We had to jump from a tree trunk, grab a rope and swing over it. One of the girls...."

"Girls?"

"Yeah – just a few – but this girl fell in *six times*."

"Did you fall in?"

"Eer... I *nearly did* once... but it was really great Trayzer,and we went sailing, and made rafts from telephone poles and petrol drums."

I could see him using his ingenuity on that.

"How long will Mum be?"

"Who can tell – Oh, look – here she is!" as Pippa parked beside us.

"How was it."

"Don't ask..." getting out of the car to give Lol a big hug.

We drive back to the village. I stay to cook him a meal while she has to go back on the job.

So good be with him again – as in Hollow-ghouli-land. How ironic. He talks and talks.- seems totally in favour of England and all its glories, -even Pop music. He couldn't stand it in Athens. He preferred Mozart when he was 14. Must have been my influence.

He tells me about Rock climbing ,which I presume to be an outdoor occupation.

"No! No, Trayzer – it's an Indoor Sport."

"An Indoor sport?" incredulous.

"Yes, Trayzer. You can't rock climb if your fingers are cold – it's very dangerous..."

'How do they climb Everest then?' No response.

The original boy has disappeared for the moment into a handsome 'cool' young man who hopes his exam results won't arrive to spoil his time with Pippa. "I'm not sure I have enough of them...." worried what Pippa will say.

But once he starts talking it pours out of him. – I learn a lot of what makes up the thrills of a young man's life in Mid-Wales – mostly about cars and what boys do with them. It makes the hair stand up on the back of my neck.

"All the kids have cars – they have to drive to the College. It is 25 miles from Ganga's. You have to have a car. I've got the reputation for being the 2nd worst driver in the College."

"What?" sure he would be an excellent driver.

"It *means*, Trayzer," with a 'fat cat' smile ," I'm the 2nd most *daring* driver in the college... the one it's most frightening to be with...."

"Oh, really?" understanding that Thrill is the object of driving, not getting from A to B safely. *Silly old me.....*

He has his own second hand Mini, which is the love of his life; it will be sometime before girls can thrill him as much as his Mini.

He has already 'written off' Ganga's car. I had heard about this.

"What speed do you think we were doing, Trayzer......."

"I don't want to think about it....."

"Promise – really promise not to tell mum..." I swear solemnly not to tell Pippa.

"It was on a small contry road, Trayzer – 3 pm in the afternoon. I had a Pal with me. The road had an elongated double bed with 'adverse camber' " filling in the technicalities, "which made the car take off into the air. It hit the ground on one wheel ripping the tyre of the hub. It rolled over twice and ended up on its 4 wheels again – pretty coool – Trayzer."

I'm in a cold sweat.

"We got out. I changed the wheel and drove home to Ganga" but he did stop at a call box to phone her the news. Of course she was so relieved that he was alive and the boy with him, she didn't give a damn about the car. It was a write off. He went on to explain that if they had been in a less roadworthy car neither of them would have lived to tell the tale. "But, if it had been my Mini – being low it wouldn't have taken off like that." Everything is a question of technicalities and sensation – not emotion.

"A pal of mine, Trayzer…" he goes on, "drives his mother's 4-wheel drive Metro across the fields to collect his sister from school."

"Across fields?"

"Yes, Trayzer at 80 mph. with induced skids in tall standing grass."

"Are you sure it's grass – not wheat."

"It's really cool, Trayzer with the trees and everything whirling around you.. One boy was killed doing it."

"How does that effect you?" curious.

"Well, it seemed really strange when we went canoeing to think he wasn't there anymore."

This is no longer the little boy who wanted to save a little coffee cup in the Easter pot throwing.

Pippa couldn't bring herself to recount her experience for several days.

"The body was unrecognisable and the stench was Awful. She had walked a good seven miles away from the hotel. Villagers say they saw this British woman playing like a child in a ditch – or running about among the olive trees like a child half naked. You know what the husband said? "Well, she's ruined my holiday.""

A few weeks later, she is convinced she has got her first grey hairs because of Mrs. Smith.

"And I've had another death to deal with. A couple on holiday, he dies of a heart attack the first week. I had to go to the hotel to explain the arrangements for flying the body home. They rang her room, she refused to come down, so, imagining she was too distraught, I went up. She was sitting on the balcony drinking ouzo. I told her the arrangements and when she would have to leave. 'I'm not going with him!' she said, 'I've got 8 days of my holiday left. We saved up for this. He wouldn't want to spoil my holiday.'"

"It's gives you a unique view of life...."

"It gives a unique view of people.... " she corrects me. ~~

29.

Lol complains about the new menagerie. "I shut them out of the house. Mum was cross with me."He seems to have developed a callousness toward animals.

"They smell, Trayzer and have fleas," he who was brought up with smelly dogs, fleas, ticks, rats, mice, hamsters, rabbits... It's true these are not his childhood friends.

Everything to him is a sick joke, the sicker the better. Was it such a good idea to push him off to England? I think it disappoints Pippa a bit too. It seems a poor return for all her effort. He was such an original child; now he has become a young hound running with the pack. This is the first time we have registered the change in him. We love him though and have faith in him.

Pip has hired a scooter for him to get about on while he's here. He has been scuba diving all week with the German School on the other side of the island

I stay over as Pippa is on duty dealing with arrests and accidents. He disappears on the scooter to join in a `Winding up' party at the Scuba diving Club on the other side of the island.

When she comes home, we have supper and go to bed.

I wake a 2.15, hearing P. come downstairs talking aloud to herself saying "It's very late...." he wasn't back. I wondered if she was sleep walking. She was prone to it as a girl when deeply disturbed. I heard her leave the house.

Fifteen minutes later I was relieved to hear the sound of the scooter in the alley beside house. He's back! But I hadn't realised she had taken the car to go and look for him, and met him entering the village.

Next morning at work, she had to deal with a scooter accident in the night – a boy of Lol's age, – having to get him transferred to an Athens hospital – in a coma and not expected to live.

"I feel I put a curse on that boy," she said later, deeply troubled in her quite way, "by worrying so much about my own.... as if some boy was going to die that night and it mustn't be mine."

Too soon we are seeing him off at the airport again…..

29.

Spend a week-end with her; she needs the company after he goes. She has three dogs again: Tosca, who is supposed to be Mr. Foti's dog but plays the two establishments to advantage. Benjie, her pup, a good natured beast, and Tig, plus Sam the cat, and now a kitten abandoned in the alley beside the house last week, which screams piercingly all the time, and has to be fed with warm milk through a tube, and she is nurturing one of the neighbour's unwanted kittens, while the mother cat inhabits the kitchen and is a thieving pest.

The other kitten can eat and move about at speed, climbing Pip's trouser leg like the trunk of a tree to get to the level of the action when Pippa is preparing supper.

Benjie washes the kittens' bums – essentially a motherly task. He is very kind and tolerant allowing the little things to crawl over his tummy looking for teats.

We spend our evening nursing one kitten each by shoving them she our jerseys in the hope of keep them quiet and peaceful. It works only while you stay put – any attempt to abandon them brings on a duplicate screaming. MIAOW! MIAOW! incessantly until you are driven mad enough to try forcing more milk into them.

The black and white Kitten is just like Damn Sam at the same age, a black and white fluffy ball on four legs with a little tail stuck straight up like a Christmas tree, and the power to move like a scud missile. Sam is appalled at the introduction of these kittens. He does not consider them of the same species as himself. He has never considered himself to be a Cat. – he is 'Damn Sam the Samurai'.

The kittens lie quietly in her hands while she de-fleas them. She can de-tick, and de-flea with her strong caressing fingernails, so they lie there in bliss. She has achieved a mad menagerie again, just what she needs. The animals rule the roost. Only animals can Lord it over her; if a person tries it, they run into a brick wall. ~~

Letter from Lawrence:

Hallo Theresa – Yes its Lawrence.

Thank you for your letter and sorry I have not written to you since. It is very nice here in Wales but not all that cold yet. It is a pity you will not be here for Christmas
    You probably know that I am doing canoeing and since last week I did not have a wet suit . It was cold very very cold but now I do, and it is all blue with a bright red chest. I can also role my canoe quite easily.
    Last Wednesday (sic) I was doing Eskimo roles in the river, with the canoe you know.
    My school subjects are very nice except the English retake – boring old English!
    Technology is very good indeed and we are learning about Electronics, hydraulics and computers most days its practical. So far I have made a car that goes towards the light, a counter for uncut contact lenses and an automatic fire extinquisher.
    It's great Mum is coming for Christmas, but I'm very sorry you will be all alone.
    I will probably be seeing you at Easter though.- God that seems a long time. I have never been away for that long, have I. It must be realy (sic) nice there and I rely do miss it – the smells I miss and the dew drops on the Spanish broom.
    Have a very nice X-mas.
    Love you ever so much
    Lawrence. XXXXXXXXX x 1000

Send my love to my cat in the form of a kiss under the chin and squeeze the dog whilst calling him Juggernaut.

He still can't spell, and has forgotten Pickle isn't with us anymore.

30.

Pippa went off to England for Christmas. As I walked in the door to take over, she said, "Oh, by the way – Tosca's pregnant again. She'll have them soon, I think. Get the Vet to put the pups down, but save one for her, though."

Well, she knows how to play her cards close to her chest! Fancy telling me now. She knows I am not the Midwife type. I am not obliged to look after her abominable animals, but would resent it if she gave the job to anyone else. She knows this.

Old Fotios, known as Foti, who lives in the front of the house, invites me to lunch on Sunday. He has good stories – he fought in the Balkan wars. He is not sure how old he is, says he was born in 18-something, which makes him over ninety. He brings me vegetables from his garden, or something he has cooked for his lunch which is a bit embarrassing. Now, if I hear him coming up the alley, I dodge out of the other door and get up on the hill behind the house. I can't take too much of him, though he is good value.

I had two social encounters today – both relating to this house. I was accosted in the alleyway by a village woman – a near neighbour, who asked politely where I came from. When I said England – she asked if I came from 'Scotia'. Why Scotland? Then it all came pouring out of her – her daughter lives in Scotland. "The *Putana English woman*, who stayed here,' jabbing a finger toward Pippa's house, "her son take my daughter to Scotland.!"

"Was that not good?"

"No! No! I never see my daughter again. I hear nothing!"

I felt very sorry for her, and did not know what to say.

In the afternoon, I sit on the front porch , the only place the sun gets to. The ruined building adjoining the house is covered thickly with ivy and makes funny trickling noises form time to time. Pippa has her washing line strung in front of it.

Glancing up from my book I saw *Kyria* Rhoda coming up the rocky path which used to be the old right of way onto the mountain. She feigns dramatic surprise to see me, and starts screaming in that powerful voice "Peppà, pou einai?" (Pippa – Where is she?)

I am sure she knows Pippa is away. and that I am in charge of the animals and the house.

"She's gone England for Christmas." as she comes to sit on the steps beside me. From what she says, I twig that she is dying to see what Pippa has done to the house, and obviously does not indulge this vulgar curiosity with Pippa herself. I take her inside. She throws up her hands at the sight of the alterations – the staircase going up from the opposite corner now; the back bedrooms gone, the upstairs transformed with *two* bedrooms *and* a bathroom. "Po'! Po'! Po '! the habitual exclamation to almost everything – nothing to do with `poo'

Downstairs she waves her arms about at the sight of yet another bathroom made in what was the corridor to the kitchen. And the kitchen – the only things remaining are the hood of the old fireplace bulging out of the wall, and the old stone sink – a crude stone trough set in the base of one of the windows. She went to this like a homing pigeon "We use to wash our faces here..." Miming like a bird in a birdbath. Pippa has some pot plants in it now. She is not poor – she probably owns lots of land, being the only survivor of her 15 siblings.

"Oh, how I remember!" she says, and talks of the wartime – the occupation. "How hungry we were. We eat nothing but *hortà*" in the literal sense `grass', but it isn't just grass. They learn from their mothers how to pick the wild greens full of goodness, though not enough to exist on totally, but full of nutrition. Now of a Sunday, you see a car stopped by the roadside and a female new bourgeoisie, with a plastic bag, knife in hand searching for this very stuff. – `Wild Greens' – now considered a delicacy.

I enjoyed her visit.

Ann came to pick me up for our regular weekly walk on the mountain. She also brought me a slice of cold turkey with stuffing and cranberry sauce, and piece of Christmas cake. Tig comes with us, and never ceases bounding over the ground hither and thither in ceaseless activity.

Back home I am looking forward to my Christmas supper of cold Turkey, plus stuffing and cranberry sauce – get the fire going – when suddenly a couple of friends arrive looking for Pippa. "She's in England for Christmas," I invite them in for a cup of tea in the sitting room. Just as I say "Do have some of the cake Ann brought me...." squeaks and squeals start coming from the kitchen. Going to investigate find Tosca giving birth to little sausages popping out of her rear end. Wouldn't she just choose this moment!

"I am afraid, the dog has chosen just this moment to give birth."

"Oh, how lovely!" Both mothers they seem thrilled.

"I'm afraid the miracle of birth is not my cup of tea" – not meaning it as a pun.

Going back to the kitchen to get more hot water, I find Tosca eating the placenta.

"She's eating the placenta now – sorry, don't mean to put you off your cake..."

"It's the best thing," one says,

"It's very nutritious.." says the other.

"The cake?"

"The placenta."

When they have gone, I find Tosca is still licking and eating the afterbirth. Pools of water and blood have stained the chair cover and formed in puddles on the floor. She is keeping her bum end out. I mop the floor.

I have a martini. Impossible to enjoy my cold Turkey and cranberry sauce. I might as well give it to the dogs.

Going into the kitchen to get another martini, I don't look toward the chair where she is, but there is such a squeaking I am forced to and find she is lying on top of her litter..

"A FINE MOTHER YOU MAKE!" having to pull them out from under her and introduce them to her teats.

The pups have been dispatched, except for the blond one. I didn't call the Vet. I drowned all but the one in a bucket. I couldn't imagine how long it would take a new born pup to drown by holding it under water... Never again! It was too late to take them out to bury them, I had to put them in the fridge, and took them up the hill next day.

Now Tosca follows me from room to room with accusing eyes "What have you done with my babies....!" I feel like a murderess..... And with the arrival of the new lot of pups, Benjie has disappeared, and Tig is going on heat. I found spots of blood on the Habitat settee. Dogs are beginning to appear from everywhere. Never do this again, Trayzer! From now on Pippa will have to find someone else to look after her menagerie.

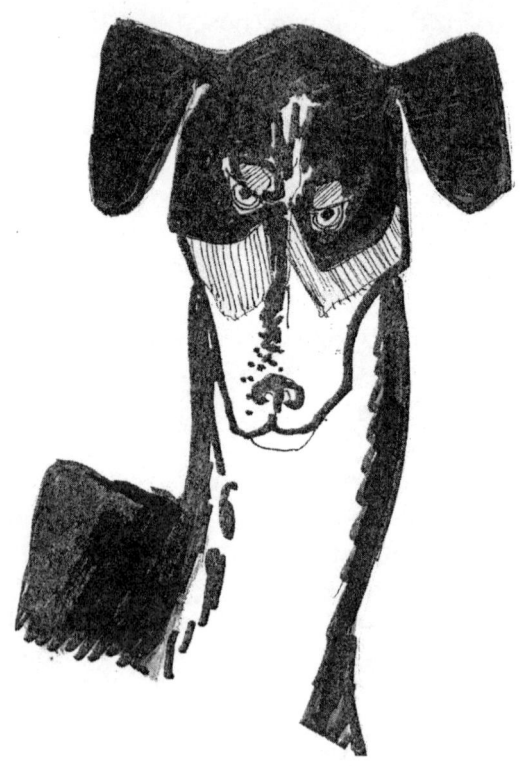

'What have you done with my babies?

30.

THE HOUNDS OF THE BASKERVILLES...

Pippa rings up – "How is it going?"

I tell her Benjie has disappeared, Tosca has had her litter, "And if that isn't enough – I do believe Tig is on heat. I thought you said she'd been spayed!"

"She has – but the Vet said it was better to leave the ovaries in – otherwise they get fat and lazy – like Nellie, remember. But it means she goes on heat."

"When will you be back?"

"That's what I'm ringing about...." her voice suddenly sounding young and rather frightened." I can't come back at present... I didn't tell you. I've got a lump. I've got to have some more tests..... perhaps an operation..."

She hadn't indicated anything was wrong. but then she always holds her cards close to her chest.

"Can you stay on ....?"

"Don't worry! I'll look after things here."

After a few more words, she goes. I find myself standing on the porch, remembering *Kyria* Rhoda as she went off down the path, stooping to pick a wild flower – and waving it over her head, "That is our life," she said, "like a flower. Gone – like a flower...." ~~

Suddenly the house is surrounded by dogs – the like of which I haven't seen outside Mediaeval manuscripts. There were no other dogs in this village until Tig came on heat – the villagers don't keep pets. These are the hounds of the Baskervilles, the dogs of nightmares, they picket the house, back and front, barking, howling, scrapping with each other day and night.

273

The Hounds of the Baskerville

Tig goes out to flirt and acquiesce, then rushes in hoping it is supper time – which it isn't. Her suitors pour up onto the back porch and squabble among themselves. It is as Greek as the suitors in Odysseus's compound, though Tig is certainly not a Penelope.

Tosca is jealous – rushing out ostensibly to chase them off with righteous indignation. She can't understand why they are not interested in her.

The kitchen door is like a stable door, which is very useful. I have a jug of water always full. When I hear them gathering I open the top section and drench them in water. It gives a little peace.

Ann comes once a week to take me for a walk on the hills. The rest of the time, I fight the animals, do the chores. As Montaigne says, `You say you have achieved nothing? But you have lived...'

In the evening, I have my typewriter on the kitchen table facing the kitchen door. Tosca is in the armchair next the stove with Jumbo, the new pup. Tig is sprawled like an odalisque on the Habitat settee recovering from the day's exertions. When I look up I see the gargoyle face of one of her `suitors' staring avidly in through the panes in the door. It gives me quite a turn. I feel I am battling with overwhelming animal forces.

Sam resents the attention I give my typewriter because I refuse to have him on my lap. He springs up onto the beam that runs across the kitchen sending down showers of dust onto my head.. The only way to deal with this , is to get up and *open the fridge door.* He hurls himself off the beam onto the hanging cupboard, drops on to the cabinet below and just as he arrives at the fridge door – I shut it. It gives me enormous satisfaction.

I have the brass `Student's lamp on the table for more light to work by. Sam likes this lamp. Instead of trying to crawl onto my lap to suckle my jersey, he sits beside the lamp basking in its glow. When I got up to replenish my glass of Retsina, I see him sitting upright warming his paws on the globe of the lamp. He even had his nose pressed to it. And I don't have a film in my camera.......

30.

The battle with overwhelming animal forces continues day and night. I've been waking up at all hours without knowing why – it must be the animal activity surrounding the house – the `suitors' spend the night on both porches, back and front. They scrap with each other. I hadn't my jug of water handy upstairs, only a tooth mug, but fill it and creep into Pippa's room, open the window and chuck it at them. Coming from a height unexpectedly, it is enough to startle them. I see them slinking off down the path. How many of them, for god's sake – five of them. I wait until they think it is safe to creep back up again, and dash another cupful down. It is enough to fill them with a superstitious fear. They retire baffled.

I feel overwhelmed by Chthonic forces both inside and outside the house. Tig – the generator of all this trouble – slinks in exhausted from her prostitution. She can hardly force down a morsel of food.

"Why go out to them, – you silly Bitch!"
"I can't help it .... I have to go....."

It isn't enough that all the chairs and the settee in the kitchen she gets up onto are spotted with blood. I came down this morning to find Tosca in my armchair – the one I brought up from the cellar so that I might have a comfortable place to sit when we're all in the kitchen with the fire. I forgot to heap things into it before going to bed. So there is Tosca lying in it on my pure wool rug saying "Yes – this _is_ a good chair. It was a good idea to bring it up, and the rug is excellent quality – very warm."

She watches my rage with a pained forbearing: "You're bringing this on yourself, you know.... if you would stop fighting us, you could be happy...."

The truth is I enjoy my rages. It's good to have something to rage at during this period of anxiety for Pippa.

I grab her by the scruff and fling her onto the floor. "Get out! Get out! and STAY OUT! You are supposed to be Foti's dog!"

"*But I haven't had breakfast yet.*"

"You are NOT GETTING ANY BREAKFAST!"

"*You can be cruel, you know.....*" looking pained but already forgiving. That look – whatever punishment I inflict on her, says, "*I know your are a <u>nice</u> person really.... nothing will make me believe otherwise....*"

Later I take her some breakfast out on the porch where she loves to sunbathe. She may be a greedy dog, but at least she never refuses anything. Tig can be a delicatessen dog. She will forego breakfast if it turns out to be boring old rice from the night before. But Tosca's greed is insatiable. She is always tottering into the kitchen just on the off-chance .... Her snuffling around every inch of the floor for any crumb, drives me insane. I seem to spend – not seem to, I *do* spend more of time cooking for them than for myself. The rest of the time is spent trying to save my rations from disappearing down their throats involuntarily. Then cleaning up the sticky mess they make on the floor. There is little energy left for Artwork! Sometimes I could hack their heads off with a carving knife!

When the sun is on the front porch – the dogs and I sit in it. Tosca on the lowest step, and dear fat Jumbo who is growing so quickly, tries to clamber up towards me by climbing on his mother's body to get onto the first of the 5 steps, but the others are too deep for him. His wobbly meandering – he can't quite support his bottom on his back legs, but they are getting stronger by the hour. To hell with Artwork.

Tig returns looking weary and disillusioned, yet when I shout at her suitors, she wearily goes back to them, like a Gipsy or a camp follower. Useless to call her back. Her kohl-marked eyes have a prostitute's sadness. She is so tired her back legs can hardly hold her up, let alone the weight of her seducers, but still she goes to with them. Those who celebrate the joys of sex – ought to notice that it has its peak and depression for animals as well as for us.

Tosca has a hard submissive will – she conquers by submission, but Tig is a truly sensitive individual – a sparkling innocent creature which makes her disillusion the more human and poignant. She wants life to be all play, good food and comfortable beds.

As Tig crawls wearily up the steps into the house, her chief lover watches from a distance. I speak to him plainly asking him to go away. He sits down. I ask him to stay away at night and keep the others away. He lies down to wait Tig's re-emergence. He is a handsome beast, dark with a tan muzzle, eyes rather close together. He is the chief of the suitors – the one she really likes. He is ready to wait for eternity. Tonight I shall have a large jug of water poised on the windowsill.

This morning she went out quite pleased to see her particular suitor, but a little later, I saw her curled up in a dejected heap in the corner of the ruin with the big dogs standing all round her. I chased them off and got her inside. I had to help her to climb onto the Habitat settee. "From now on STAY INSIDE! YOU STUPID CREATURE! I won't mind if you pee and shit on the floor "

I had just got them out of the habit by berating them every night, before going upstairs. "Now DON`T YOU DO ANYTHING HERE.! " standing on the place where they always do it. They yawn and say, *"Oh, you do go on ...."*

She couldn't look at food and slept until I was having a cup of coffee and some buttered toast. At the sound of the toaster clicking up, she was roused to interest. So I made her a plateful of buttered toast! which she managed to get down.

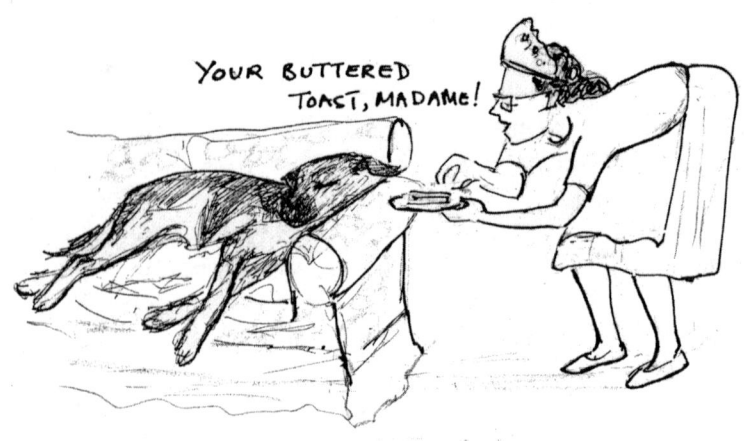

The suitors are all around the house – big powerful brutes. I want to find Lawrence's catapult. I'm sure I saw it in the cellar under the kitchen. I find something much better – his air pistol and some pellets to go with it. My brother taught me to use an air pistol when I was a kid. Of course I won't fire at them, but I can fire at the walls all around them. I feel like a Frontiers woman under threat from the Injuns – quite crazed with antagonism.

31.

'PEES-CRAP HALL'

But the pup is fun – he is getting big so quickly, I called him `Jumbo'. I can almost see him growing in his sleep. He shows signs of intelligence. I watch him think things out. How to get up steps. He can take himself to his draught proof box when his mother has left him on the cold draughty floor.

Everything is lovely to a pup, chewing his mothers ears, sucking her dugs. Sleep is wonderful, waking is fun. He worships my feet, because the plate of food comes down from above them, so whenever he encounters my feet, he wags his tail, happily embracing them nearly has me down.

But he will pee on the rug, he finds the floor too cold. He can't understand why he is picked up and placed on the cold floor again and insists on waddling onto the rug to widdle in comfort. He widdles and poos all over the kitchen with a joyous abandon.

I call this place 'Pee's Crap Hall' now , and make up a rhyme about it.

PEE'S CRAP HALL

Terds,..Terds.. Glorious Terds
Nothing quite like 'em
To get on her nerves;
Wherever we do 'em
We're made to rue 'em
But we'll always do 'em
GLO-OR-OR-EE -US TERDS!

The Cat sleeps between my sheets
Which makes them
Hairy, nitty, gritty
And make me Sneezy- wheezy
Which does not please me !

I stick these in an envelop and send them to her, hope they'll makes her laugh. The good news is that she will be out of hospital soon – home with Ganga – after just one week.

Looking for something to read on the bookshelves I found a daily diary written by Pippa when she was 17, with brief terse entries. At the end of each entry she records what she had for supper. Fascinating to see the references to food – she, who is constantly dieting. She blocks off food in her life now.

~~*Monday*: `I dislike Mondays intensely. Had discussion after School on Euthanasia. Life is a challenge but sometimes I wish it was a more exciting challenge – I think everyone needs to be brave and have a hope in order to live a good life. I also think everyone should be used to their full extent and should not be allowed to wander – or something like that. These ideas are just forming. Shepherd's Pie.*
~~*Tuesday:* `Alain must write – Fish.'*
~~ ***Wednesday:*** *`I have lost a bit of weight. I want to be happy. – Fish.'*
~~*Thursday: Hair can go in a Tom Jones style. Would like a new dress for weekend. Liver.*
~~*Friday: Must clear up these beastly spots – they are erupting yet again. Read. Finished Chaucer. Going to make a dress. Lovely chops.*

~~ ***Saturday:*** *Sat and talked and almost missed lunch. Great pity as it was corned beef, potatoes and beetroot as well.*

She reviews every month at the end of it. New month. New experiences.

~~ `Read more Virginia Woolf. Steak.
~~ '....want new friends. Shepherds Pie. '

That is what she needs – new friends and a new life now that Lol is going to be far away most of the time. I can see why she has these awful animals. You need to fill this house with something – to come back to day after day, especially at night.

Tig watching Tosca feeding the puppy

32.

THE BATTLE GOES ON

At least Tig has learned to keep inside the house – now the problem is to keep the dogs Out! *How Long , O Lord.... how Long – is this bitch going to be on heat?* I have to bolt the front door, or heavy though it is, they push it open and I come upon the beasts in the sitting room. This goes on at night too. They hammer and scratch at the front door under the porch below my window. But now I have the Air Pistol on the window ledge ready. Last night I fired at the enamel bowl on the ground outside. That got them slinking off down the path. I hit it again when they tried to sneak back.

It will be February on Saturday. I surrender to the sun on the front porch with a jar of Retsina. At night I barricade them into the kitchen to keep the dogs from sleeping on the settees in the sitting room. Tig is still bleeding like a stuck pig all over the cover on the kitchen settee, though I have given her some old towels, she manages to rearrange them so that her blood gets onto the cotton covers.

This evening, having let the Spanish main go out, I went up to bed, then had to come down for my book and found Sam sitting in the old enamel cook-pot on the top of the stove, cooking himself gently on the remaining heat. Cat casserole!

Sam sitting inthe Casserole

Ann picked me up for our weekly walk though I no longer feel up to it I'm so worn out fighting the animals. It was an excellent walk, cold and bracing. It did me good to see a large expanse of sky .The air made me quite lightheaded at first. The view of the Albanian mountains over the powder blue sea is magnificent, their dinosaur backs snow crested.

When we got back she stayed for a cup of tea. We took it out onto the porch in the sun – Tosca lies sunbathing on the bottom step, and Jumbo manages to struggle up the steep steps to get to us. I had the air pistol on the table so the moment a dog appears I fire at the walls above him – Zap! he scarpers. I gives me enormous satisfaction, though I don't think Ann quite approved.

"Its the only thing that has any effect!"

Life is more peaceful since I've been sapping at the dogs from the upstairs window. It has got them rattled.

In the evening, furious with Tosca I kicked her out, told her to go to Mr. Foti. After all, Jumbo doesn't need her now. Went to bed early, lights out before ten. Now Tosca takes her sweet revenge by hiccupping her relentless bark in the porch below my window. Determined not to let her in, I lie there fighting her in my head. She barked continuously from 10 till 11.20.

She won. I went down called her in. Dipping and curtsying with her nervous tick: 'Oh, did you call? How sweet of you to let me in…I know you are a nice person really…' The double dyed deceiver! Having won the victory she settles happily in the kitchen, while I stamp upstairs back to bed.

Then Tig, seeing that Tosca got attention, starts barking in the sitting room at nothing at all. I fling myself downstairs again, bellowing her into a shocked silence.. Up I go again, nerves aflame. It takes an hour to come off the boil and fall into some sort of sleep for an hour or two.

But poor Tig, being more sensitive than Tosca, she has taken to heart my admonitions not to pee or poo in the kitchen and asks to be let out for calls of nature – only to be set upon by the suitors. This morning on opening the sitting room door into the small vestibule between it and the kitchen I discover two large piles of poo and pee. Tig had got through the barrier I put up between the kitchen and sitting room and done it there. She had *tried* <u>not</u> to do it in the kitchen. You just can't win with this game.

A phone call from Pippa with the thrilling news – she hopes to get back as soon as the radiation treatment is finished. "I hope the house and the animals are behaving...." she says.

Oh, yes – they are `behaving'.- and how! They have me right under their paws.

The dictionary definition is: Behave: to function in a particular way...

Now I am running out of food for the animals. I intend to feed them only once a day from now on. They used to expect breakfast. Sally, at my urgent request brought up some tins of Dog food. None of the animals – (Tosca excepted – who will eat anything even poo) will touch it. What the hell puts them off? It looks good. I could eat it myself. Is that the end of it ? – I eat what the dogs leave? Everything is possible in this situation.

Since I have hardened my heart against them, I am having a more peaceful time of it. There must be a moral in this somewhere – a rather depressing one. The world is not based on Love, but greed, and self-interest just like the animal world. Nature is ruthless and totally without sentiment.

The latest insult is to find the sneaky little cat from next door asleep on my bed. She darts into the house like a shadow whenever I open the door. I found her on my bed again this evening. She's almost ready to have kittens. That would be the last straw – to find the neighbour's grotty little cat having kittens in the middle of my bed! Is there no end to this experience?

The almond blossom is out all through the village – so lovely – like a wedding procession. If only Pip were here to see it.

Took Jumbo puppy for his first excursion into the Big Wide World – down to the Bakery on the bottom road. He enjoyed it to the utmost. How he can tug on the lead. He's only 6 weeks and two days old. He managed the steep steps and galloped along pulling me behind him. I want him to know his environs properly so he can find his way back if he runs off, as he surely will do the moment he is big enough. He is now sleeping off the experience at my feet and dreaming in squeaks of adventures still to come.

Made a spectacle of myself in the village this morning, with the two dogs and the pup on a lead. We gambled through the village street getting disdainful looks – this not being an English Village. I was wondering if I would have the courage to go into the butchers to ask for some bits and pieces for the dogs. I went first to the little shop where I buy rice and chocolate. I tied Jumbo up outside, but the man came out and made nice noises at Jumbo.

I had to screw myself up to tackle the butcher. I bought some odd bits and pieces, but when I boil them up for the dogs, they turn their nose up at it. I boiled it up with rice. Tig won't eat rice but likes fried bread.

What a lecture I gave the animals – not to pee or poo on anything. They did me the honour to sit and listen to my cogent arguments. Tig listened politely and gave a discreet yawn. Jumbo smiled trustingly. Sam sat on the top of the fridge, scowling "This has nothing to do with me...." which is true enough. Only Tosca huddled down in her chair pretending to be asleep and beyond criticism. All this *before one's morning cup of tea!* My attempts to house-train Jumbo surprise and mystify him – even amuse him! He obligingly ate his own shit this evening. His mother cleared off what was left. They are trying I suppose....

Animals! they can't open doors, or shut them – yet they are always wanting to be in when out, and out when in. They can't carry logs for the fire, yet stretch themselves out all over the hearth so you can't get near it yourself.

Tonight, I decided to have *an animal free evening.* I shut them into the kitchen, and myself alone in the sitting room to watch a video. Sam managed to get in, but I refuse to have the cat vampiring my jumper whenever I am comfortably settled. I flung him back into the kitchen, and shut the door. For the rest of the evening he howled and picked at the door in a fury of frustration, but my heart is becoming like stone towards pets of any kind. I have serious doubts about the whole `pet' syndrome which is a substitute for our failed emotions. My good nature toward them has completely shriveled up. Now I don't even speak to them. The result is magical. All is peace – until supper time. My silence is more effective than my thunder. I really have reached the point when I could brain them with a mallet – even the puppy. He was making such a noise last night, play-fighting with his mother, I gave him a sharp slap. At which he walked right across the kitchen and sat thoughtfully on the mat by the kitchen door for a whole 20 minutes, before he decided it was safe to return to the fire where he sat quietly and went to sleep.

Oh, Joy! She rang this morning saying she will be back on Friday!

I've scowered the house, made up her bed , and given the animals such a lecture on not peeing and pooing in front of the fridge. Tonight they are all quiet like good children, determined to be seen and not heard.

Do they know she's is coming back tomorrow?

Pippa walks into the kitchen looking a New Woman. She had gone straight to the Consulate to do a morning's work before coming home. The house breathes again and the animals are content. I have the first really good night's sleep in the back room. No scratchings at the door, no whimperings and barkings.

Pippa has lots of new clothes.

"Ma and I went on a shopping binge before I came away. Can you help me turn up this skirt." part of a magenta pink suit.

"Where do you want the hem, then..." kneeling on the floor with a mouthful of pins.

"Above the knee.." she says firmly. This is a new Pippa.

And, "Can you stay on – I've got to attend a conference at the Embassy in Athens next week – it will be only three days. ....."

"After three months, what are three days." ~~

34.

WITCH BITCH!

The moment she walks out of the house to go to Athens, the animals revert to 'behaving'. They feel insecure again without her – and that makes them more demanding of me. Weird.

Ann came to pick me up for the weekly walk. When we come back, she comes in for the customary mug of tea. For some reason, instead of taking our tea onto the porch, I say, "Oh, let's have it in the kitchen."

Two minutes later, as we are sitting at the table; there is a roaring sound and the house shakes violently.

"Good God! Was that an earth tremor?"

Going into the sitting room – a new light is coming through the window where it was dim before. Ann follows me. "The ruin has fallen down!" I stand in the doorway looking out on a sea of rubble – the porch where we might have been sitting is broken with a pile of stones on the steps. "What if we had been sitting there!"

Shouts and wailings come from Foti's area – the stones have flung themselves into his little garden and broken through the wall of the kitchen built onto the side of the house. I run down to see if he is alright, and find the neighbours wailing and gesticulating – but Mr. Foti is quite unperturbed, – though he was sitting in the kitchen when it happened – the stones stopped short of his foot. "Bah!' he says, "I fought in the Balkan Wars – It takes more than this to disturb me.!"

Back in the house, I stand again at the front door looking at the mess. Tosca? She sunbathes on that lower step. Where is she? She's not here. Then I hear it..... a whimper....

"Oh, My God, Ann! Tosca is under there and she's not dead..." thinking what it must mean – broken to bits but not dead. She wouldn't be dead – would she – not her! Another whimper confirms it.

What do I do now? Positively hating her for have a ton of stones on her and not being dead! For doing this to me!

Ann turns tail – "Oh, I cant bear this sort of thing, I'm going home.. I'll ring you later....." Well – That's a bit much, feeling like the boy *standing on the `burning deck whence all but he had fled.'*

There is only one thing to do...... searching in Pippa's telephone book for the number of the Embassy in Athens.

"Can I speak to ....., please. It is urgent. She is at the Conference."

"I'm sorry we can contact her now – would you like to leave a message and I will get her to call back."

"Please tell her – her wall has fallen down."

"Oh!"

I put down the phone, and return to gaze out from the sitting room door, praying for Silence...... she has to be dead....... she *must* be dead... willing her to be dead. Another whimper comes. How is one to find her under all this stone – she could be anywhere...... To think Ann and I might have been sitting there...... We have had a miraculous escape – Mr. Foti too is uninjured – only this bloody dog..........

The telephone rings. Pippa: "What's happened? What wall has fallen down?"

"The ruin! And …" *Should I tell her?* "and ..That's not all.... Tosca is under the rubble..... and she's alive.....I can hear her whimpering."

Pippa takes command even from a distance, piloting my reeling imagination through the shoals of ineptitude. She knows what a Moral Coward I am. "Go down the lane – find Yanni... Tell him to get men to dig her out."

Which Yanni? They all have the same names – there could be half a dozen Yannis down any lane.

"But I'll need to get a Vet up here –" The idea of sitting with a smashed dog for hours waiting for a vet to come and put her out of her misery.

"First of all, get them to dig her out," says Pippa firmly.

I go back to the door wondering how to set about the task. If only the damn dog was dead.

At this point in my dilemma, I see a man coming up the path towards the house. I call out, "There is a dog trapped under here... Can you find some men to get her out...."

He doesn't respond, perhaps its my Greek...or is he the Village Idiot...sheer curiosity must have brought him up here. He just plods across the fallen rubble towards the broken porch.

He stops just below me, bends down to lift a big stone – at which Tosca pops out like a Jack-in-the-Box! shaking herself to throw off clouds of thick white dust. He must have seen her snout poking up between the stones – which I couldn't see. I reel back into the sitting room thinking only: `Now I must get a Vet to her....'

When I look again – I think I am hallucinating. There is Tosca standing on all four feet shaking clouds of dust from her coat; not a broken bone, not a drop of blood! She is not even trembling. Perfectly composed, she bobs up the rest of the way into the sitting room, still shaking herself to get rid of the dust.

`TOSCA!' flinging my arms around her. I have never loved that dog – but I love her *now!*. I always knew she was a Witch – but I didn't know what kind of a witch. A blessed Witch Bitch for letting me off the hook.

I quickly phone the Embassy to get a message through to Pippa in the conference that the dog is alive and quite okay. Straight away she rings back to listen to the amazing story.

"When the message was given me in the Conference – everybody burst out clapping!" Typically British.

I give Tosca a very special supper. She is totally composed and not even her simpering self. Witch Bitch! She is a born survivor after all.

34.

Pippa. got back this morning, she went to the front porch to look at the devastation. She stood there a long time. How many times has she been out there pinning up the washing on the line. She wouldn't have had a chance.....

In the evening we watch a video without any animal interference.

"It isn't like this when I am alone here – Tig would even stand in front of the television so I couldn't see it! "

"Why didn't you shut them out."

"I did but they whined and cried and barked – and threw themselves at the door. I tell you they don't give me a moment's peace. I think it must be to do with security. You are their Real Person. I am not, so I must be manipulated constantly to ensure their survival because I might just walk away and not come back. You – though you walk out of the kitchen every morning – are bound to return. Yet, I am the one stuck with them ALL DAY. I *can't* escape *them!*"

There has to be some truth in this but she just laughs convinced it's just me being me.

I told her my dream – that she had returned with 3 intensely lively black kittens who flew everywhere, plus two snow white Pekinese and a peculiar hairless calf with skin that fell in folds. There was yet another dog hanging about only half seen. I protested feebly, you said in your Pipperish way: "Oh, but they are perfectly sweet – you'll get used to them." The rest of the dream was spent telling people "You know what she did? she brought back 3 kittens, 2 Pekinese a cow-calf, and another stray dog. But Tomorrow I will go home to an `animal free' zone.!'" and told her she must not go away again. Nothing would persuade me to look after her animals again

A month later: I am back in the house looking after the dogs. Pippa is not alright. She has gone back to England, to see what they can do for her.

3 weeks later: There is nothing to be done. It is only a matter of time. She will not be coming back.
    I must close up the house. Jan has taken Tig and Sam. Sally has taken Jumbo. Tosca goes back to Mr. Foti. PoxyPercy disappeared months ago. I take a final look round, seeing that everything is off, the windows and shutters secure, and exit by the kitchen, turning the key twice, try the handle. I take the key to Mr. Foti – who sighs saying he has had enough of life, and doesn't want any more of it. *But she is only 45.........*
    "Ach! Panayia Mou!"...he sighs again.
    I leave him, go down the path to the road to wait for the bus.

A year later........

It's Lawrence's 21st Birthday!
   Thinking of him – wondering how he is – suddenly, I hear a soft mewing. It seems to be just outside my door at the top of my stairwell. That's strange. ...this really is an `animal free zone'. All the stray cats have disappeared. There are no cats around in our neighbourhood – I haven't seen a cat for months.
   Puzzled, I open my door. A beautiful pure white young cat gazes up at me sweetly, walks past me into my room fearlessly and gracefully examining things right and left. The cats on the path are wild and untamable. Whenever they got into the stairwell, they would panic. It was difficult to get them out. But this one.....
   I am convinced of one thing, and one thing only: *This has to be Pippa's doing...... It has her signature all over it.* It's Lawrence's 21st Birthday and this cat, a pure white cat, walks in and takes me over. Pippa wants me to do something…..... I have to share this with somebody…..... I go to telephone her sister in Wales. Penny answers straight away.. Usually I get the answer phone which they never answer.
   "Trayzer!"
   I gabble out the story of the White Cat. "It has to be Pippa's doing! It's Lol's 21st. There has to be a connection."
   " Gosh.... Yes....... . Thank you for ringing...."

Two weeks later – a letter from Penny:

"After you'd phoned about the cat on Lawrence's birthday I was so happy! I told Lawrence on the way out to his 21st Birthday dinner

celebration. He was really pleased. We were taking him to a nice restaurant out in the country.

When we got to this restaurant , a big fluffy <u>White Cat</u> she came <u>straight</u> to Lawrence, climbed all over him, and stayed on his lap all evening. The restaurant Owner was surprised too. "I've never seen that cat do that before. She doesn't like people....." ~~

Lol's letters:.

Dear Trayzer – sorry you have not heard from me for so long. I am now on a ski holiday in France and having a great time. I am now at Brighton Uni doing Environmental studies which is pretty hot stuff.

I think I may have been a little enthusiastic with the ski on the first day. i.e. today because my leg is a tad knackered – still that's life. Loads of love. Lawrence XXXXXXXXX

Hi Trayzer, I've just spent 10 weeks working for my dad down in London. I went to Ireland for the summer. It was amazing. I windsurfed and beach bummed all summer – God What a Life!

I've got a surf van to go to Terrifa in as well and shoot some tubes, so basically all is amazing. Loads of Love and have a blistering Crimble. i.e. Christmas. XXXXXXXXX

Hello Trayzer! Thank you for the card. I can't rembre if I told you anything when I wrote so let me outline significant developments. I'm at Brighton doing something or other quite interesting. But! I'm now well into Diving – in fact so well into it I would like to persue a carrier in commercial diving so I've decided to take next year out of UNI in order to get the appropriate qualifications and hopefully a job. If I still like it, I won't return to UNI next year....

I am now, and have been for some time, the extremely proud owner of a GPZ 1100 Kawasaki – 5 years ago this was the fastest production bike in the world. Mine is in shit state of course hence a very low price – the bike has been down on numerous occasions but I'm working on it and its beginning to shine through. I am also and have been for a year an advanced driver but you wouldn't know it! They even asked me if I would consider going on an instructors course for the institute. I said I would but never did – the truth be known most advanced drivers I found are experts on the highway code but can't bloody drive!

Oh, by the way Happy Easter. It's Easter Sunday today. I have not bought any Easter eggs cause everyone is too fat and don't deserve them.

Lots of Love. Lawrence. XXXXXXXXXXXX

~~~~~~~~~~~~~~~~~~~~~~~

He still can't spell for toffee nuts.....

August : the hottest on record: 104° degrees. I have just had my second or third shower , standing starkers in my bedroom next the front door, when I hear masculine footsteps coming up the stairwell. Instead of stopping at the flat below, they continue on up to my door – the finger belonging to the feet, presses my bell. I hate that bell – I don't want anybody ringing my bell.... I don't open the door.

"*Pious einai?* (Who is it?)"
"Egó.. (Me)"
"*Ti thelis ?* What do you want?"
" Esí – (You.)"
" Ekané Láthos... I think you've made a mistake...."
"*Oxi – (No)*" the relentless masculine voice replies.

Suddenly, a slight inflection in the voice triggers something in my brain.

"Hang on! I think I KNOW WHO IT IS!" Struggling into my cotton rags, I fling open the door and myself into the arms of the young man leaning nonchalantly against the wall. "You said you were coming Last Year!"

"We're a year late that's all...." he coolly replies.

Behind him on the stair stands a young woman, patiently holding two dogs on one lead. "This is Nikki." by way of introduction. They all slouch into my pad which is never geared to receive visitors. "This hasn't changed, Trayzer."

"You mean it's the same mess.... an *Artistic* mess! " I insist defensively. " But, more to the point, where have you come from?"

"Spain.... we drove down in the van. We've come straight from the ferry boat. We need a swim.... we thought we'd pick you up. "

The irresistible invitation!

I have to dig out my swimsuit I haven't used for years, before following them down the path to clamber into the van, with the patient dogs to drive the half-mile to the Causeway. "You remember when we used to swim over to the island with the dogs – on the airbed!"

"Lets do it now."

"You two can swim it with the dogs. I'm going to ride in the pay boat," because the past is flooding back and will sink me. I watch them enter the water, followed by the dogs. On the island we swim from the same rocks we used to swim from....... the boy is 28 now.

"Where will you camp tonight?"

"Up there," he says definitively. His first home.

In the morning they pick me up again. Lawrence's first words are, "It's not the same, Trayzer..." referring to the house where he grew up. "It's not loved anymore."

I know what he means. The old oak door has been painted white to resemble the fashionable aluminum doors they put on houses now. The garden is sterile where two large guard dogs run up and down.

"We could go and look at the other house. I think it is on the market again. " The house, empty for three years, was sold eventually to an English woman . I ring the agent to borrow the key. They said the owners had taken the house off the market.

"Damn! But we can show Nikki the outside."

"Okay, let's go."

Leaving the Van in the car park at the end of the village we toil up the steep path toward the house, but all we can do is peer in through the panes in the kitchen door.

"Oh, look – there's the Spanish Main! Remember getting that in place?"

"Yeah, Trayzer, and you trying to persuade us not to....."

"Oh, shut up – you don't have to remember that."

"There's the collection of old keys on the wall just where they always were."

"Gosh, so they are. I had completely forgotten them."

So many things, just the same, though the cupboards have been painted a rather nice turquoise blue -

"I wonder if my Big Teddy is still in there..." he says, pacing like a panther through the back alley to the front porch. He batters at the door , willing it to let us in, but it doesn't yield to his strong fists or to a shoulder charge. The frustration at not being able to get inside becomes intense. Looking up at what used to be Pippa's bedroom, the shutters never did quite close, I have to suppress the feeling that she is looking down at us with amusement.

Returning to the back alley, he manages to lift off one of the shutters on the ground floor back bedroom. We peer in. " I used to sleep in there. That's the iron bedstead that used to be in your room, Lol. The curtains are the ones she made. So much of her still in there – her DNA built into the fabric of it. It is still *Her* House. He puts the shutter back. This is so frustrating.

Lawrence casually says, "I'm just going back to the Van to get my keys...." and disappears down the alleyway. Nikki and I sit on the stoop with the patient dogs Lawrence reappears with his collapsible chair over one shoulder. He goes up onto the kitchen porch, positions himself on the chair in front of the kitchen door.

"This may take some time.... it can go easily ...or it could take half an hour. Do you remember which way the lock turns, Trayzer."

"Oh, Gosh no..." not daring to ask what he intends... glad the kitchen porch is up this unused alleyway where nobody is likely to pass. Nikki is equally silent. We are all in collusion.

With quiet concentration he works at the keyhole. "How did you....." I venture to ask – unnecessary to frame the question....

"My Dad..." (his Greek parent) " installs security systems" (in England) " you have to be a locksmith... if anything goes wrong with it...."

"Oh, yes. I can see that...."

"You can buy these keys in any DIY in England, Trayzer..."

"Really? That's handy..."

"There's one gone...." he says in quiet triumph. "Two more to go..." A few more minutes of wrapt concentration, then "There's the last!"

He opens the door. I spring up the steps like a cat. "Leave our shoes outside, Kids – and don't let the dogs in – foot and paw marks would be fatal...." How a coward becomes a Burglar's Moll.

We tiptoe into the kitchen in bare feet – Nikki follows me closely as I point to things that belong to Pippa. "That's her.... that's her.... she brought that back from...."

Followed closely by Nikki, I tread softly through into the sitting room as if in a Faery world, exclaiming in a whisper.... "That's the settle the dogs used to sleep on... those are her pictures just as she put them...."

We tiptoe up the stairs.... the thrill of her presence everywhere. There are changes but nothing alters the character of the house she created. It is her house still, her things in it, her essence in full force – her achievement.

Lawrence follows taking his time, scanning everything with his lazer beam eye, heat-seeking her. He always scrutinizes everything intensely – absorbing its essence.

Changes have been made, but nothing alters the character of the house she created. The improvements are congenial. I have a strong impression she approves them, the new colour schemes just as she might have made them herself in the same period of time.

In the bathroom the stenciled frieze she painted on. "*She* did that – she brought the stencils back from England...." It is her house still, her personality ineradicable .

"Come on , Kids – don't lets push our luck. This is breaking and entering you know...." having a sudden horror of the owners arriving at this very minute at the airport for their summer holiday... heading toward us. "Lets get the hell out of here..." my natural cowardice reasserting itself.

The dogs wag their tails with relief at the sight of us. We all clamber back into the Van to go for a swim at a remote beach. On the way back into town, he says, "We want to go to the cemetery ...where's a flower shop..." One appears by magic by the roadside with plenty of space to park the van. They go into the shop arm in arm, and emerge with one single white rose.

Outside the British Cemetery – they park the van, comb their hair, clean their teeth, put on clean T-shirts, before we push the gate that rings the sweet toned bell and enter the Victorian World of posturing sandstone grief for dead sailors, young Victorian wives who died in childbirth, and babies who served no other purpose than grief.

We walk up the avenue of cypress to find the simple plaque fixed to the low wall – the place she chose herself – 'next to Mrs. Fish.'

With arms about each other, the two young people debate what to do with the single white rose. There is no jar, no water – it is so hot no bloom can survive. They lay it carefully on the top of the wall. Lawrence produces a candle from St. Spiridon's church "We got it yesterday..." says Nikki. Kneeling, he scrapes a groove between the stones like a farmer planting a seed, lights it. – a gust of wind promptly blows it out.

"Pippa wouldn't want us to burn the cemetery down..." I murmur... Wild fires have been rampaging through the island this year. He doesn't relight it.

We have supper in town. They drive me home, dropping me off at the bottom of my path. They are going tomorrow.

"I am not saying Goodbye!" embracing Nikki who has so patiently absorbed the reminiscences which would have bored another girl to death. Lawrence gives me a rib-cracking hug. I walk resolutely up the path. He calls:. "Trayzer – give us another hug..."

I turn back to receive another crushing .... the curtain has been lifted. Pippa, the dogs, cats, rats, mice, tortoises, rabbits, ducks, Budgies and – Love birds – all the joys of the experiences which tie us together will always be there. We are still afloat on `Pippa's Ark'...... and always will be.......

~~~~~~~~~~~~~~~~~~~~~~~~~~~~~~~~~~Corfu 2005